New Syllabus

MATHEMATICS WORKBOOK 1

Consultant:
Dr Yeap Ban Har

Authors:
Teh Keng Seng BSc, Dip Ed • **Loh Cheng Yee** BSc, Dip Ed
Joseph Yeo MEd, PGDE (Distinction), BSc (Hons) • **Ivy Chow** MEd, PGDE, BSc

shinglee publishers pte ltd

SHINGLEE PUBLISHERS PTE LTD
120 Hillview Avenue #05-06/07
Kewalram Hillview Singapore 669594
Tel: 67601388 Fax: 67623247
e-mail: info@shinglee.com.sg
http://www.shinglee.com.sg

First Published 1992
Reprinted 1992, 1993, 1994, 1995
Revised Edition 1997
Reprinted 1997, 1998
Revised Edition 1999
Reprinted 1999
Revised Edition 2000
Reprinted 2001, 2002, 2003, 2004, 2005, 2006
Revised Edition 2007
Reprinted 2007

ISBN 978-981-237-323-6

Cover design by Dave Cheong

Acknowledgement

The authors and publishers are grateful to:

Key Curriculum Press for permission to use screenshots of activities created
using The Geometer's Sketchpad and the website address www.keypress.com.

Printed in Singapore by Mainland Press Pte Ltd

PREFACE

New Syllabus Mathematics Workbook (Express) is written in line with the new Singapore-Cambridge GCE 'O' Level Examination and the new initiatives of the Ministry of Education.

The workbook consists of exercises which prepare students for their examinations. The more difficult questions are marked with an ∗.

To encourage student-centred learning, the workbook includes non-routine types of worksheets that are classified under the section, **Alternative Assessment**. These worksheets encourage students to learn independently through carefully-guided steps and the use of IT. Students are motivated to investigate mathematical concepts with various methods and think critically, so that they will understand and appreciate the concepts better. The teacher can gauge the students' learning by assessing the work with the scoring rubric found at the end of the relevant worksheets. The workbook is accompanied with a CD-ROM that contains templates to be used with some worksheets.

It is hoped that with the use of various pedagogies, different types of students will be inspired to achieve success in mathematics.

Mario Bannick.

Links to Internet Resources

Chapter	Topic	Subject	Links
1	Factors and Multiples	Know more about Goldbach Conjecture	http://mathworld.wolfram.com/GoldbachConjecture.html
6	Number Sequences	Know more about Fibonacci sequence	http://library.thinkquest.org/27890/applications5.html

If the links are not active, please email josephbw.yeo@nie.edu.sg
In the meantime, you can use a search engine to search for alternative websites.

CONTENTS

Chapter 1 Factors and Multiples

1. A **prime number** is a number which has only two different factors, 1 and the number itself. Prime numbers are 2, 3, 5, 7, 11, 13, 17, etc.

2. A **composite number** is a number which has more than two different factors. Composite numbers are 4, 6, 8, 9, 10, 12, 14, 15, 16, etc.

3. The number 1 is neither a prime nor a composite number because it has only one factor.

4. A composite number can be expressed as the product of two or more prime numbers.

5. The process of expressing a composite number as the product of prime factors is called **prime factorisation**.

6. Index notation:
    In general, $\underbrace{a \times a \times \ldots \times a}_{n \text{ factors}}$ is written as a^n and is read as a to the power of n.

7. The largest of the factors common to two or more numbers is called the **Highest Common Factor (HCF)** of the numbers.

8. The smallest of the common multiples of two or more numbers is called the **Least Common Multiple (LCM)** of the numbers.

9. If a number y can be expressed as $y = x^2$, we say that y is the **square** of x and x is the **square root** of y.
    If x is a whole number, then y is a **perfect square**.

10. If a number y can be expressed as $y = x^3$, we say that y is the **cube** of x and x is the **cube root** of y.

Practice Questions

1. Find the sum of all prime numbers less than 30.

2. Find the sum of all prime numbers between 80 and 100.

3. Find the sum of the first three prime numbers that end with a 9.

4. Find the difference between the two prime numbers between 20 and 30.

Express the following numbers in prime factors.

5. 315   **6.** 3234   **7.** 8008

8. 61 200   **9.** 58 752   **10.** 117 800

Find the H.C.F. of the following.

11. 16 and 24   **12.** 45 and 63   **13.** 56 and 70

14. 90 and 126   **15.** 1008 and 1960   **16.** 1080 and 1584

17. 42, 66 and 78   **18.** 84, 98 and 112   **19.** 132, 156 and 180

20. 195, 270 and 345   **21.** 147, 231 and 273   **22.** 225, 495 and 810

Find the L.C.M. of the following.

23. 30 and 24   **24.** 72 and 48   **25.** 75 and 105

26. 243 and 405   **27.** 306 and 144   **28.** 264 and 504

29. 1176 and 1960   **30.** 435 and 261   **31.** 104, 56 and 72

32. 450, 720 and 1170   **33.** 324, 972 and 756   **34.** 16, 28, 44 and 68

35. 180, 90, 126 and 36

Find the H.C.F. and L.C.M. of the following.

36. 189 and 84   **37.** 315 and 720   **38.** 616 and 392

39. 1008 and 1764   **40.** 560, 140 and 224   **41.** 378, 567 and 252

42. 792, 1188 and 330   **43.** 525, 1400 and 315

44. Find
     (a) the difference between the first two perfect squares that end with a 9.
     (b) the sum of the first three perfect squares that end with a 4.
     (c) the first two perfect squares whose difference is 20.
     (d) the product of the first two perfect cubes that end with a 1.
     (e) the difference between the first perfect squares and the first perfect cube that end with a 5.

45. Write down all the perfect squares and perfect cubes that are between 50 and 600.

Using prime factorisation, find the square root of each of the following.

46. 2304   **47.** 7056   **48.** 2025

49. 3969   **50.** 9216   **51.** 3136
52. 8281

Using prime factorisation, find the cube root of each of the following.

53. 5832   **54.** 9261   **55.** 17 576

56. 39 304   **57.** 59 319

Evaluate the following.

58. $\sqrt[3]{64\,000\,000}$

59. $\sqrt{160\,000}$

60. $9^2 \times 2^3 - \sqrt{289} + \sqrt[3]{1331}$

61. $[(132 + \sqrt[3]{1728} - \sqrt{441}\,)] \div 4^2 \times 15^3$

62. $60^3 \div \sqrt{625} - \sqrt[3]{2744} - \div \times 19^2$

Estimate mentally the following.

63. 51^2

64. 69^2

65. 302^2

66. 19^3

67. 62^3

68. 398^3

69. $\sqrt{48}$

70. $\sqrt[3]{65}$

71. $\sqrt[3]{998}$

72. $\sqrt{626}$

73. $11^3 + \sqrt[3]{7999}$

74. $19^2 \times \sqrt{10\,004}$

75. $\sqrt{99} - \sqrt[3]{28}$

Use a calculator to evaluate the following.

76. $69^3 + 126^2 - \sqrt{71\,289} \times \sqrt[3]{912\,673}$

77. $\sqrt[3]{12\,167} \times 57^2 - 56^3 \div \sqrt{153\,664}$

78. $(\sqrt{576} + \sqrt{961} - \sqrt[3]{12\,167}\,) \div \sqrt[3]{4096} \times 37^3$

79. $(\sqrt{292\,682} - 7^3) \div 3^2 + \sqrt{1\,290\,496} - \sqrt[3]{35\,937} \times \sqrt{1089}$

80. $18^3 \div \sqrt{5184} + (16^2 - \sqrt[3]{753\,57}) \div (22^3 - 103^2 - \sqrt[3]{753\,571}\,)$

*81. Canteen *A*, Canteen *B* and Canteen *C* repeat their lunch menus every 12 days, 8 days and 10 days respectively. All canteens are serving noodle soup today. In how many days later will all the three canteens be serving noodle soup again?

*82. Mrs Lim has sponsored a total of 105 hot dogs and 126 cans of fruit juice for the refreshment of a class picnic. Each pupil will receive the same amount of refreshment.
   (a) What is the greatest number of pupils that the refreshment can cater to?
   (b) How many hot dogs will each pupil receive?
   (c) How many cans of fruit juice will each pupil receive?

*83. A World Bank conference is being attended by 96 members from China, 72 from Japan and 48 from Korea.
   (a) What is the greatest number of discussion groups that can be formed so that members from each country are distributed equally among all the groups?
   (b) How many members from China will there be in each group?

*84. James was trying to sleep one night but there was too much noise around him. His clock ticked every 20 seconds; a tap was dripping every 15 seconds and his pet dog snored every 27 seconds.
   He noticed on his clock that all the three events happened together on the stroke of midnight.
   (a) After how many minutes would all the three events happen together again?
   (b) How many times would all the three events happen together again between midnight and one o'clock?

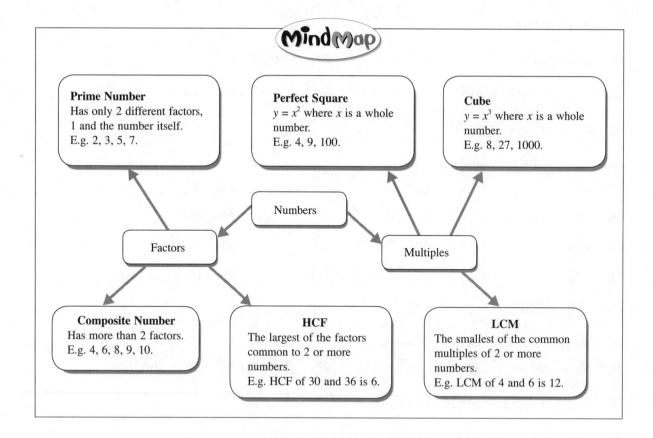

Mathematical Investigation: Prime Numbers

Section A: Prime Numbers

- 1, 2, 3, 4, 5, … are called **_natural (or counting) numbers_**.
- A **_prime number_** is a natural number that has only two different factors. For example, 7 is a prime number because it has only two different factors: 1 and 7.
- A **_composite number_** is a natural number that has more than two different factors. For example, 6 is a composite number because it has more than two different factors: 1, 2, 3 and 6.
- The number 1 has only one factor, so it is neither a prime nor a composite number.

1. Eratosthenes of Cyrene (276–194 BC), an African, invented a method to sift out the prime numbers. We will use this method, called the **_Sieve of Eratosthenes_**, to sift out prime numbers less than 100. Consider the table of 100 numbers below.

    Step 1:   Cross out the number **1** because it is not a prime number.
    Step 2:   Circle the next number **2** because it is a prime number.
                     Then cross out all the other multiples of 2, i.e., 4, 6, 8, 10, 12, … because they are not prime numbers.

Step 3: Circle the next number **3** because it is a prime number.
Then cross out all the other multiples of 3, i.e., 6, 9, 12, 15, ... because they are not prime numbers. Some numbers, such as 6, have already been crossed out in Step 2.

Step 4: The next number **4** has already been crossed out, so it is not a prime number.

Step 5: Circle the next number **5** because it is a prime number.
Then cross out all the other multiples of 5, i.e., 5, 10, 15, 20, 25, ... because they are not prime numbers.

Step 6: The next number **6** has already been crossed out, so it is not a prime number.

Step 7: Circle the next number **7** because it is a prime number.
Then cross out all the other multiples of 7, i.e., 7, 14, 21, 28, 35, ... because they are not prime numbers.

Continue this process until all the numbers have been circled or crossed out.   **[2]**

1	2	3	4	5	6	7	8	9	10
11	12	13	14	15	16	17	18	19	20
21	22	23	24	25	26	27	28	29	30
31	32	33	34	35	36	37	38	39	40
41	42	43	44	45	46	47	48	49	50
51	52	53	54	55	56	57	58	59	60
61	62	63	64	65	66	67	68	69	70
71	72	73	74	75	76	77	78	79	80
81	82	83	84	85	86	87	88	89	90
91	92	93	94	95	96	97	98	99	100

2. How many prime numbers are there that are less than 100?   **[1]**

_____

3. Write down all the even prime numbers. How do you know your list of even prime numbers is complete?   **[1]**

_____

_____

4. Can a 2-digit number ending with the digit 5 be a prime number? Why or why not?   **[1]**

_____

5. *Twin primes* are prime numbers that differ by 2. For example, 3 and 5 are twin primes because the difference between these two primes is 2. Write down all the twin primes less than 100. How many pairs are there?   **[1]**

_____

_____

New Syllabus Mathematics Workbook 1

6. In the table below, the formulae $6n + 1$ and $6n + 5$ are used to generate all the prime numbers **greater than 3**. For example, when $n = 0$, $6n + 1 = 6 \times 0 + 1 = 1$ and $6n + 5 = 6 \times 0 + 5 = 5$. Complete the rest of the table. **[2]**

n	$6n + 1$	$6n + 5$
0	1	5
1		
2		
3		
4		
5		
6		
7		
8		
9		
10		
11		
12		
13		
14		
15		
16		

7. Which numbers in the above table are prime numbers? How many are there? **[1]**

_____

8. Which prime numbers (greater than 3) are missing from the above table? **[1]**

_____

Section B: Goldbach's Conjecture

9. The even number 4 can be written as the sum of two primes, i.e. $4 = 2 + 2$. Express the following even numbers as the sum of two primes. **[1]**

$4 = 2 + 2$
$6 =$
$8 =$
$10 =$
$12 =$
$14 =$
$16 =$
$18 =$
$20 =$

10. Is there more than one way to express some of the above numbers as the sum of two primes? If yes, give an example. [1]

_____

11. Is there any even number that can be expressed as the sum of two primes in 3 ways? If yes, give an example. [1]

_____

12. The even years in this decade are 2002, 2004, 2006, 2008 and 2010. Express them as the sum of two primes. There is more than one way. To help you, a list of prime numbers is given below. [1]

2002 =

2004 =

2006 =

2008 =

2010 =

Prime numbers between 900 and 1100:

907	911	919	929	937	941	947	953	967	971
977	983	991	997	1009	1013	1019	1021	1031	1033
1039	1049	1051	1061	1063	1069	1087	1091	1093	1097

Conclusion

13. Write down one main lesson that you have learnt from this worksheet. [1]

_____

_____

Internet Resources

Christian Goldbach (1690-1764), a Russian, made this conjecture in 1742: any even number greater than 2 can be expressed as the sum of two primes. So far, no one has been able to prove **Goldbach's conjecture**. A counter example cannot be found, but that does not mean that the conjecture is true. In fact, Oliveira e Silva has shown on 30 Dec 2005 that all the even numbers from 4 up to 3×10^{17} can be expressed as the sum of two primes. So if you want to prove it wrong, you must find a counter example that is greater than 3×10^{17}! For more info, visit the appropriate website (see Preface).

Final Score:

⬚ **/ 15**

Final Score	12–15	10–11	8–9	6–7	0–5
Grade	A	B	C	D	F

Teacher's Comments (if any):

_____

_____

Mathematical Investigation: Polite Numbers

You have learnt in this chapter that a natural number can be written as the product of its prime factors, For example, $12 = 2 \times 2 \times 3$. In this worksheet, you will investigate when a natural number can be written as the sum of consecutive natural numbers, For example, $12 = 3 + 4 + 5$.

Note: 0 is not a natural number.

Section A: Sum of Two Consecutive Natural Numbers

1. The odd number 9 can be written as the sum of two consecutive natural numbers: $9 = 4 + 5$. Express the following odd numbers as the sum of two consecutive natural numbers. If it is not possible to do so, indicate 'Not possible' beside the number. **[1]**

    $$1 = \quad +$$
    $$3 = \quad +$$
    $$5 = \quad +$$
    $$7 = \quad +$$
    $$9 = 4 + 5$$
    $$11 = \quad +$$

2. What pattern(s) do you notice in Q1? **[2]**

    _____

    _____

3. Using the pattern(s) you identify in Q2, express 2007 as the sum of two consecutive natural numbers. **[1]**

    _____

4. Do you think all odd natural numbers, except 1, can be written as the sum of two consecutive natural numbers? Why or why not? **[2]**

    _____

    _____

5. How many ways can the number 9 be written as the sum of two consecutive natural numbers? Why? [2]

_____

_____

6. Express the following even numbers as the sum of two consecutive natural numbers. If it is not possible to do so, indicate 'Not possible' beside the number. [1]

   2 = ___ + ___
   4 = ___ + ___
   6 = ___ + ___
   8 = ___ + ___
   10 = ___ + ___

7. Do you think all even natural numbers can be written as the sum of two consecutive natural numbers? Why or why not? [2]

_____

_____

Section B: Sum of Three Consecutive Natural Numbers

8. The number 9 can be written as the sum of three consecutive natural numbers: $9 = 2 + 3 + 4$. Express the following numbers as the sum of three consecutive natural numbers. If it is not possible to do so, indicate 'Not possible' beside the number. [2]

   1 = ___ + ___ + ___
   2 = ___ + ___ + ___
   3 = ___ + ___ + ___
   4 = ___ + ___ + ___
   5 = ___ + ___ + ___
   6 = ___ + ___ + ___
   7 = ___ + ___ + ___
   8 = ___ + ___ + ___
   9 = ___ + ___ + ___
   10 = ___ + ___ + ___
   11 = ___ + ___ + ___
   12 = ___ + ___ + ___

9. By looking at the pattern in Q8, do you think which numbers can be written as the sum of three consecutive natural numbers? Why? [2]

_____

_____

10. How many ways can the number 9 be written as the sum of three consecutive natural numbers? Why? **[1]**

_____

_____

Section C: Sum of Four Consecutive Natural Numbers

11. Which numbers can be written as the sum of four consecutive natural numbers? Investigate. Try to explain why it happens. **[4]**

Section D: Multiples of Odd Numbers

12. The *multiples* of 9 are 9, 18, 27, 36, 45, ... We will try to express the multiples of 9 as the sum of consecutive natural numbers. Continue the pattern below. **[1]**

    9 =   4 + 5

    18 =   3 + 4 + 5 + 6

    27 = ____ + 3 + 4 + 5 + 6 + ____

    36 = ____ + ____ + 3 + 4 + 5 + 6 + ____ + ____

    45 = ____ + ____ + 3 + 4 + 5 + 6 + ___ + ____ + ____

    54 = ____ + 3 + 4 + 5 + 6 + ___ + ___ + ____ + ____

    63 = 3 + 4 + 5 + 6 + ____ + ___ + ___ + ____ + ____

    72 = 4 + 5 + 6 + 7 + ____ + ___ + ___ + ____ + ____

    81 = 5 + 6 + 7 + 8 + ____ + ___ + ___ + ___ + ____

13. Using the same pattern as above, express the first six multiples of 7 as the sum of consecutive natural numbers. **[1]**

    7 =

    14 =

    21 =

    28 =

    35 =

    42 =

14. Do you think all multiples of odd natural numbers (other than multiples of 1) can be written as the sum of consecutive natural numbers? Why or why not? **[2]**

    _____

    _____

15. Which numbers cannot be written as the sum of consecutive natural numbers? By looking at all the previous questions, write down the first 6 numbers that cannot be written as the sum of consecutive natural numbers. What do you notice about these numbers? **[2]**

    _____

    _____

    Another way to answer Q15 is to open the appropriate Excel file from the Workbook CD. The file will show a table of numbers that can be written as the sum of consecutive natural numbers.

Section E: Sum of Consecutive Natural Numbers

16. The number 9 can be written as the sum of consecutive natural numbers in exactly two different ways (order of the consecutive natural numbers is not important):

$$9 = 4 + 5$$
$$9 = 2 + 3 + 4$$

   Express the number 18 as the sum of consecutive natural numbers in exactly two different ways. [1]

   _____

17. Find a number that can be written in exactly three different ways and show the three different sums. [1]

   _____

   _____

18. Find a number that can be written in exactly four different ways and show the four different sums. [1]

   _____

   _____

Conclusion

19. Write down one main lesson that you have learnt from this worksheet. [1]

   _____

   _____

Final Score:

[   ] / 30

Final Score	24–30	20–23	15–19	10–14	0–9
Grade	A	B	C	D	F

Teacher's Comments (if any):

_____

_____

Chapter 2 — Integers

Summary

1. **Integers** are: ..., –4, –3, –2, –1, 0, 1, 2, 3, 4, ...

2. **Addition of Integers**
   (a) For any two negative integers $-x$ and $-y$,
   $$-x + (-y) = -(x + y).$$

   (b) For a positive integer x and a negative integer $-y$,
   $$x + (-y) = x - y \quad \text{if } x > y \quad \text{and} \quad x + (-y) = -(y - x) \text{ if } y > x.$$

3. **Subtraction of Integers**
   For any two integers a and b, $a - b = a + (-b)$.

4. **Multiplication of Integers**
   For any two positive integers x and y,
   (a) $x \times (-y) = -(x \times y)$ and $(-x) \times y = -(x \times y)$,
   (b) $x \times y = +(x \times y)$ and $(-x) \times (-y) = +(x \times y)$.

5. **Division of Integers**
   For any two positive integers x and y,
   (a) $0 \div x = 0$ and $0 \div (-x) = 0$,
   (b) $(-x) \div y = -(x \div y)$ and $x \div (-y) = -(x \div y)$,
   (c) $x \div y = +(x \div y)$ and $-x \div (-y) = +(x \div y)$.

Practice Questions

Do not use calculators unless stated otherwise.

1. If 10 km south is indicated by –10, how would you indicate 10 km north?

2. If +100 indicates a profit of $100, how would a loss of $91 be indicated?

3. If a deposit of $600 is represented by +600, how would you represent a withdrawal of $60?

4. If 5 flights down is represented by –5, how would you represent 14 flights up?

5. Write down the larger number in each case.

    (a) −1, −2   **(b)** −6, 6   **(c)** −7, 3

    (d) 0, −3   **(e)** 1, −10

6. Write down the smaller number in each case.

    (a) −30, 7   **(b)** $\dfrac{-12}{2}$, −5   **(c)** 0, $\dfrac{-4}{5}$

    (d) −1, 0   **(e)** −13, 12

Add the following.

7. $(-2) + (-2)$ **8.** $(-5) + (-9)$ **9.** $(-11) + (-12)$ **10.** $(-1) + 1$

Evaluate

11. $(-2) \times (-3) \times (-4) \times (-5)$ **12.** $(-8) \times (-3) \times 5 \times (-6)$

13. $(-2) \times 5 \times (-9) \times (-7)$ **14.** $4 \times (-4) \times (-5) \times (-16)$

15. $5 \times 6 \times (-1) \times (-12)$ **16.** $(-1) \times (-8) \times 3 \times 5$

Evaluate the following.

17. $56 \div (-7)$ **18.** $625 \div (-5)$ **19.** $(-75) \div (-25)$

20. $(-100) \div (-4)$ **21.** $140 \div (-7) \div 4$ **22.** $(-264) \div 11 \div 8$

23. $(-390) \div (-13) \div (-5)$

Evaluate the following.

24. $[(-3) + (-4)] \div 7$ **25.** $(-56) \div [7 + (-14)]$ **26.** $(-9) \times (-4) \div (-12)$

27. $\dfrac{(-2) \times (-5) + (-20)}{(-10)}$ **28.** $\dfrac{(-123) \times [19 + (-19)]}{38}$

29. An airplane descended 150 m from an altitude of 650 m and then ascended 830 m immediately. At what altitude was the airplane flying?

30. Beginning with a temperature of 24°C, the temperature rises by 8°C, then drops by 14°C and finally rises by 2°C. What is the temperature after the above changes?

31. An officer from the Food and Veterinary Department measures the mass of 5 packets of rice. Each packet of rice is supposed to contain 1 kg of rice. The table below shows the results. Fill in the blank and hence find the average mass of the 5 packets of rice.

Packet	1	2	3	4	5
Amount below or above the required mass (g)	−28	−13	+10	−19	+5
The actual mass (g)					

32. A surveyor measures the water levels of 4 reservoirs in 3 months. The result are shown in the table below.

	Reservoir	A	B	C	D
Water level below or above the standard mark (cm)	April	–2	+1	–3	–5
	August	+6	+3	–1	+9
	December	+8	–7	–2	–1

(a) Find the average water level, in cm, of each reservoir in the 3 months.
(b) Which reservoir caught the most rain in the year?
(c) Which reservoir caught the least rain in the year?

33. Five students participated in a science quiz. Marks were deducted for wrong answers. Their scores in 3 quizzes are shown below:

	Alan	Bob	Carol	Den	Eileen
Quiz 1	–22	–15	+90	+83	+71
Quiz 2	+34	–30	–11	+44	–19
Quiz 3	–18	–7	–21	–29	+33
Total Score					

(a) Fill the total score of each student in the table.
(b) Who had the lowest total score?
(c) The winner of the quiz was the student with the highest total score. Who was the winner?

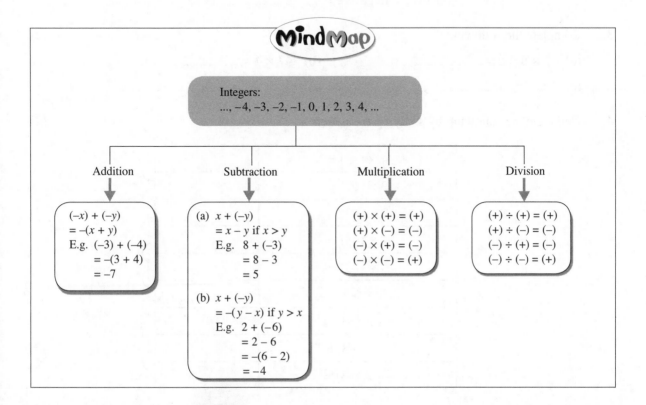

Exploratory Worksheet: Multiplication of Negative Numbers

1. Complete the following by studying the pattern.   **[2]**

$4 \times 3 =$	
$3 \times 3 =$	
$2 \times 3 =$	
$1 \times 3 =$	
$0 \times 3 =$	
$-1 \times 3 =$	
$-2 \times 3 =$	
$-3 \times 3 =$	
$-4 \times 3 =$	

-3

2. A **negative** number times a **positive** number equals a _____ number.   **[2]**

negative $\times$ **positive** = _____

positive $\times$ **negative** = _____

3. Complete the following: **[2]**

   (a) $-2 \times 6 =$ _____   **(b)** $-7 \times 4 =$ _____

   (c) $3 \times (-5) =$ _____   **(d)** $4 \times (-3) =$ _____

4. Complete the following by studying the pattern.   **[2]**

$4 \times (-3) =$	
$3 \times (-3) =$	
$2 \times (-3) =$	
$1 \times (-3) =$	
$0 \times (-3) =$	
$-1 \times (-3) =$	
$-2 \times (-3) =$	
$-3 \times (-3) =$	
$-4 \times (-3) =$	

$+3$

5. A **negative** number times a **negative** number equals a _____ number. [1]

$$\textbf{negative} \times \textbf{negative} = \underline{\hspace{3cm}}$$

6. Complete the following: [1]

(a) $-4 \times (-5) =$ _____   (b) $-8 \times (-6) =$ _____

7. Summary of Worksheet: [1]

$$\textbf{positive} \times \textbf{positive} = \underline{\hspace{3cm}}$$

$$\textbf{negative} \times \textbf{positive} = \underline{\hspace{3cm}}$$

$$\textbf{positive} \times \textbf{negative} = \underline{\hspace{3cm}}$$

$$\textbf{negative} \times \textbf{negative} = \underline{\hspace{3cm}}$$

Real-life Examples:

8. Think of real-life situations to explain *why* a negative number times a positive number will give a negative number. [2]

_____

_____

_____

9. What about real-life situations to explain *why* a negative number times a negative number will give a positive number? [2]

_____

_____

_____

Final Score:

◻ / 15

Final Score	12–15	10–11	8–9	6–7	0–5
Grade	A	B	C	D	F

Teacher's Comments (if any):

_____

_____

What conclusions can you draw about the sum of the squares of any three consecutive even integers? Write down clearly how you come to these conclusions. You get more marks for generating interesting and novel answers. You should give as many solutions as possible.

Scoring Rubric

Competency Level	Conceptual Understanding	Creativity	Mathematical Communication
4	• Showed complete understanding of the mathematical concepts involved • Used appropriate mathematical terms	• Included a variety of conclusions and some original ideas	• Gave clear and complete conclusions
3	• Showed nearly complete understanding of the mathematical concepts involved • Used nearly correct mathematical terms	• Included a variety of conclusions	• Gave fairly complete conclusions
2	• Showed understanding of some of the mathematical concepts involved • Used many wrong mathematical terms	• Included many conclusions but of limited variety	• Gave vague conclusions
1	• Showed limited understanding of the mathematical concepts involved • Misuse of or failure to use mathematical terms	• Included many irrelevant conclusions	• Gave conclusions which were difficult to understand
0	• Showed no understanding of the mathematical concepts involved • Failure to use mathematical terms	• Included totally irrelevant conclusions	• Gave muddled conclusions
Score			

Final Score:

 / 12

Final Score	10–12	8–9	6–7	4–5	0–3
Grade	A	B	C	D	F

Teacher's Comments (if any):

_____

_____

Rational Numbers

 **Summary**

1. Rational Numbers

A rational number is a number which can be expressed in the form $\frac{a}{b}$, where a and b are integers and $b \neq 0$. A rational number can be expressed as a terminating or a recurring decimal.

2. Real Numbers

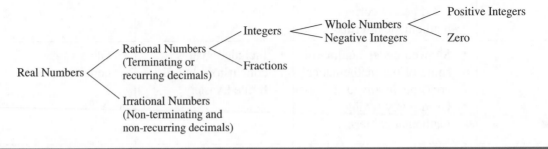

 **Practice Questions**

Do not use calculators unless stated otherwise.

Evaluate the following, expressing each answer in the simplest form.

1. $-2\frac{1}{3} - \left(-1\frac{1}{2}\right)$

2. $\frac{2}{5} - \left(-\frac{1}{6}\right)$

3. $-\left(-1\frac{1}{5}\right) + \left(-1\frac{1}{3}\right)$

4. $2\frac{5}{9} - 3\frac{1}{4}$

5. $2\frac{1}{4} + \left(-1\frac{3}{5}\right)$

6. $-\left(-\frac{7}{8}\right) - 1\frac{3}{4}$

7. $9\frac{1}{4} + \left(-7\frac{3}{5}\right)$

8. $-4\frac{2}{9} - \left(-1\frac{1}{6}\right)$

9. $-2\frac{3}{4} + \left(-1\frac{1}{2}\right) - \left(-1\frac{2}{3}\right)$

10. $-6\frac{4}{9} - 3\frac{3}{4} - 3\frac{5}{9}$

11. $-\left(-3\frac{4}{7}\right) + 1\frac{2}{5} - \left(-\frac{3}{7}\right)$

12. $\frac{2}{3} - \left(-3\frac{3}{20}\right) + \left(-\frac{2}{5}\right)$

13. $-3\frac{4}{5} - 1\frac{3}{10} - \left(-2\frac{3}{4}\right)$

14. $\left(-\frac{1}{2} + \frac{1}{3}\right) + \left[\frac{1}{4} + \left(-\frac{1}{3}\right)\right] + \left(-\frac{1}{20}\right)$

Evaluate the following. Express each answer in its lowest terms.

15. $5 \times \left(-2\frac{2}{5}\right)$

16. $(-16) \div \left(-\frac{4}{5}\right)$

17. $16\frac{3}{10} \times (-5)$

18. $\left(-\frac{7}{18}\right) \times \left(-\frac{9}{14}\right)$

19. $\left(-\frac{4}{9}\right) \times \left(\frac{3}{14}\right)$

20. $15\frac{1}{6} \div (-5)$

21. $\left(-\frac{5}{6}\right) \div \left(-\frac{3}{4}\right)$

22. $\left(-7\frac{1}{3}\right) \div 1\frac{5}{6}$

23. $\frac{9}{11} \div \left(-\frac{4}{5}\right)$

24. $(-4) \div \left(-\frac{1}{4}\right) \times (-4)$

25. $\left(-2\frac{2}{5}\right) \times \frac{5}{6} \div (-13)$

26. $1\frac{7}{15} \div \left(-17\frac{2}{7}\right) \times 3\frac{3}{14}$

27. $\left(-2\frac{5}{7}\right) \div \left[1\frac{1}{3} \times \left(-\frac{3}{4}\right)\right]$

28. $3\frac{3}{5} \times (-6) \div \left(-4\frac{4}{5}\right)$

Simplify the following.

29. $20 \times \left(\frac{3}{4} - \frac{4}{5}\right)$

30. $\left(\frac{7}{27} - \frac{5}{36}\right) \times (-9)$

31. $\left(\frac{1}{4} - \frac{3}{4}\right) \div \left(-\frac{1}{4}\right)$

32. $\left[\left(-9\frac{1}{4}\right) - \left(-7\frac{3}{5}\right)\right] \div 2\frac{3}{4}$

33. $\left(-\frac{3}{4}\right) \times 1\frac{1}{2} + \frac{3}{4} \times \left(-2\frac{1}{2}\right)$

34. $\frac{1}{4} + \left(-\frac{3}{4}\right) \times \left(-1\frac{1}{4}\right)$

35. $\left(-12\frac{1}{2}\right) + 1\frac{2}{3} \div (-4) - \frac{5}{7} \times \left(-2\frac{4}{5}\right)$

Use a calculator to evaluate the following. Give your answers correct to 3 decimal places.

36. $\left(0.4658 - 3\frac{2}{15}\right) \times \left(-1\frac{11}{13}\right)$

37. $\sqrt{246} \times (-0.555) \div (-1.2389)$

38. $\left(-11\frac{6}{17}\right) \div \left(5.96 - 9.368 \times 2\frac{6}{17}\right)$

39. $[-4.749 - 6.558 \times (-2.094)^3] \div \sqrt[3]{-1.999}$

40. $\pi \times (4.119)^2 \div (2.008) + \left(31.709 - \frac{\pi \times (8.143)^2}{7.985}\right)$

41. $-\sqrt[3]{-65.678} \times \sqrt[3]{37.089} - \pi \times [(-3.917) \div (-2.007)]^2$

42. $\left[\left(2.75 - 13\frac{2}{9}\right) \div \left(-11\frac{5}{7}\right) - \left(-12\frac{3}{5}\right)\right] \times \left(-\frac{55}{97}\right)$

43. $\left\{\left(\frac{1}{3}\right)^2 - \sqrt[3]{\frac{8}{33}} \times \left[-\sqrt{\frac{5}{6}} - (-0.375)^3\right]\right\} \times [-\pi \div (-6.5)]$

In each of the following cases, write down **(a)** the largest value and **(b)** the smallest value.

44. $\dfrac{1}{2}, \dfrac{2}{3}, \dfrac{3}{4}, \dfrac{4}{5}$

45. $\dfrac{9}{16}, \dfrac{3}{5}, \dfrac{11}{20}, \dfrac{23}{40}$

46. $\dfrac{5}{6}, \dfrac{13}{15}, \dfrac{23}{30}, \dfrac{14}{18}$

47. $\dfrac{7}{20}, 0.39, 0.4, \dfrac{11}{25}$

48. $0.8125, \dfrac{43}{48}, \dfrac{5}{6}, 0.875$

Arrange the following in ascending order.

49. $\dfrac{7}{10}, \dfrac{13}{20}, \dfrac{2}{3}$

50. $\dfrac{13}{20}, \dfrac{11}{15}, \dfrac{3}{4}$

51. $\dfrac{13}{15}, \dfrac{5}{6}, \dfrac{37}{45}$

52. $\dfrac{5}{12}, \dfrac{7}{18}, \dfrac{11}{27}$

Arrange the following in descending order.

53. $\dfrac{2}{3}, \dfrac{3}{5}, 0.7$

54. $\dfrac{14}{25}, \dfrac{26}{59}, \dfrac{11}{20}, \dfrac{53}{100}$

55. $\dfrac{19}{27}, \dfrac{2}{3}, \dfrac{13}{18}, \dfrac{7}{9}$

56. $\dfrac{17}{24}, \dfrac{5}{8}, \dfrac{2}{3}, \dfrac{11}{16}$

57. A shirt is sold at $\dfrac{3}{8}$ of its original price. Given that the shirt costs \$32 originally, find its selling price.

58. Alvin, John and Peter buy a business. Given that Alvin pays $\dfrac{3}{10}$ of the cost price and John pays $\dfrac{9}{20}$ of it, what fraction of the cost price does Peter pay? If Peter pays \$7000, how much does the business cost?

59. A farmer uses $\dfrac{11}{18}$ of his field for growing rice and $\dfrac{3}{7}$ of the remaining field for growing tomatoes. Of the area thus left, he uses $\dfrac{1}{4}$ of it to grow spinach and the rest to grow sweet potatoes. What fraction of the field is used for growing sweet potatoes?

60. A man left $\dfrac{3}{7}$ of his money to his wife, $\dfrac{1}{2}$ of the remainder to his brother and the rest of it to be divided equally among his three children. If each of his children received \$400, how much did his wife receive?

Express the following fractions as recurring decimals.

61. $\dfrac{5}{9}$

62. $\dfrac{8}{11}$

63. $\dfrac{17}{66}$

64. $\dfrac{11}{12}$

65. $\dfrac{17}{33}$

66. $\dfrac{29}{18}$

67. $\dfrac{37}{44}$

68. $\dfrac{19}{48}$

69. $\dfrac{55}{72}$

70. $\dfrac{47}{45}$

71. $\dfrac{100}{99}$

72. $\dfrac{100}{999}$

Use a calculator to evaluate the exact value of the following.

73. $1.9^2 + 1.9 \times 0.4$

74. $12.6 + 7 \times 0.5$

75. $28.2 - 28.2 \times 0.1 + 0.9$

76. $4.8 \times 12.5 - 25.76 \div 3.2$

77. $36.36 \div 1.8 + 20.8 \times 3.05$

78. $(1.25 \times 2.7 \times 5.1) \div (8.1 \times 0.25 \times 1.7)$

79. $(5.36 + 7.46) \div 13 \times 0.01$

80. $6.4 - 2.88 \div 4.5 + 1.6 \times 0.85$

81. $\dfrac{4.176 + 2.9 + 37.6 \times 3.1}{0.59}$

82. $\dfrac{63.2 \times 2.8}{5.53} + \dfrac{2.826}{0.9 \times 1.57}$

83. $\dfrac{4.72 - 3.8 + 1.04}{12.5 - 12.43} - \dfrac{6.33 - 5.15 \times 0.84}{0.167}$

84. $0.36 \div [0.36 - (2.16 \div 6 - 0.01 \div 0.25)] \times 0.9$

85. $40\dfrac{9}{10} - 3.45 \times 1\dfrac{2}{5} - 8.6 \times 3\dfrac{9}{20}$

86. $\left[1.8 + 1\dfrac{9}{10} \times (5.9 - 3.8)\right] \div \left(1.41 - 1\dfrac{2}{5}\right)$

Journal Writing: Rational or Irrational?

Some of your friends claim that π is an irrational number because $\pi = 3.14159\ 26535\ \dots$ is a non-terminating and non-recurring decimal and so it cannot be written as a ratio of two integers $\dfrac{a}{b}$. But other friends claim that π is a rational number because π can be written as $\dfrac{22}{7}$. Explain to your friends, in your own words, the difference between rational and irrational numbers that you have learnt in class and give examples where necessary. Then explain why π is a rational or an irrational number.

Scoring Rubric

Competency Level	Conceptual Understanding	Mathematical Communication
4	• Showed complete understanding of the mathematical concepts involved • Used appropriate mathematical terms	• Gave clear and complete conclusions
3	• Showed nearly complete understanding of the mathematical concepts involved • Used nearly correct mathematical terms	• Gave fairly complete conclusions
2	• Showed understanding of some of the mathematical concepts involved • Used some wrong mathematical terms	• Gave vague conclusions
1	• Showed limited understanding of the mathematical concepts involved • Misuse of or failure to use mathematical terms	• Gave conclusions which were difficult to understand
0	• Showed no understanding of the mathematical concepts involved • Failure to use mathematical terms	• Gave muddled conclusions
Score		

Final Score:

 / 8

Final Score	7–8	6	4–5	3	0–2
Grade	A	B	C	D	F

Teacher's Comments (if any):

_____

_____

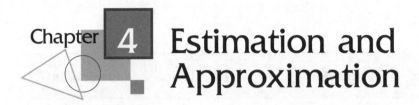

Chapter 4 Estimation and Approximation

Rules for rounding a number to a given number of significant figures:

(a) Count the given number of significant figures from left to right, starting with the first non-zero figure. Include one extra figure for consideration.

(b) If the extra figure is less than 5, drop the extra figure and all other following figures. Use zeros to keep the place value if necessary.

(c) If the extra figure is 5 or more, add 1 to the previous figure before dropping the extra figure and all other following figures. Use zeros to keep the place value if necessary.

Rules for determining the number of significant figures:

(a) The following figures in a number are significant:
    (i) All non-zero figures.
    (ii) All zeros between significant figures.
    (iii) All zeros at the end of a decimal.

(b) The following figures in a number are not significant:
    (i) All zeros at the beginning of a decimal less than 1.
    (ii) All zeros at the end of a whole number may or may not be significant. It depends on how the estimation is made.

Do not use calculators unless stated otherwise.

Make an estimate and pick the closest answer in each of the following cases.

1. $4.95 \times 201.99 =$
    (A) 10   **(B)** 100   **(C)** 1000   **(D)** 10 000   **(E)** 100 000

2. $4971.3 \times 223.74 =$
    (A) 1 000 000   **(B)** 100 000   **(C)** 10 000   **(D)** 1000   **(E)** 100

3. $24\,940 \times 9.956 =$
    (A) 250   **(B)** 2500   **(C)** 25 000   **(D)** 250 000   **(E)** 2 500 000

4. $4761 \times 589 =$
    (A) 300 000 000   **(B)** 30 000 000   **(C)** 3 000 000   **(D)** 300 000   **(E)** 30 000

5. $7938 \div 0.038\ 755 =$
   (A) 200　　　　　**(B)** 2000　　　　　**(C)** 20 000　　　　　**(D)** 200 000　　　　　**(E)** 2 000 000

6. $8.184 \times 0.8888 =$
   (A) 0.64　　　　　**(B)** 0.72　　　　　**(C)** 6.4　　　　　**(D)** 7.2　　　　　**(E)** 64

7. $31\ 990 \times 5800 =$
   (A) 18 000　　　　　**(B)** 180 000　　　　　**(C)** 1 800 000　　　　　**(D)** 18 000 000　　　　　**(E)** 180 000 000

8. $112.19 \div 0.3977 =$
   (A) 2500　　　　　**(B)** 250　　　　　**(C)** 25　　　　　**(D)** 2.5　　　　　**(E)** 0.25

9. $8.01 \div 0.0421 =$
   (A) 2　　　　　**(B)** 20　　　　　**(C)** 200　　　　　**(D)** 2000　　　　　**(E)** 20 000

10. $5891 \times 32\ 810 =$
   (A) 0.02　　　　　**(B)** 0.2　　　　　**(C)** 2　　　　　**(D)** 20　　　　　**(E)** 200

Estimate each of the following and select the nearest answer in each case.

11. $\dfrac{59.26 \times 5.109}{3.817} =$
   (A) 0.75　　　　　**(B)** 7.5　　　　　**(C)** 75　　　　　**(D)** 750　　　　　**(E)** 1500

12. $\dfrac{16.02 \times 0.0341}{0.079\ 21} =$
   (A) 0.006　　　　　**(B)** 0.06　　　　　**(C)** 0.6　　　　　**(D)** 6　　　　　**(E)** 60

13. $\dfrac{89.82}{10.713 \times 0.028\ 15} =$
   (A) 3000　　　　　**(B)** 300　　　　　**(C)** 30　　　　　**(D)** 3　　　　　**(E)** 0.3

14. $\dfrac{9.034 \times 0.2106}{0.0289 \times \sqrt{24.778}} =$
   (A) 0.012　　　　　**(B)** 0.12　　　　　**(C)** 1.2　　　　　**(D)** 12　　　　　**(E)** 120

15. $\dfrac{2905 \times (0.512)^3}{0.004\ 987} =$
   (A) 750　　　　　**(B)** 7500　　　　　**(C)** 75 000　　　　　**(D)** 750 000　　　　　**(E)** 7 500 000

16. $\dfrac{4.311 \times 0.029\ 16}{\sqrt[3]{981} \times 0.0231} =$
   (A) 60　　　　　**(B)** 6　　　　　**(C)** 0.6　　　　　**(D)** 0.06　　　　　**(E)** 0.006

17. Round off the following.
    (a) 5623 km to the nearest 10 km
    (b) 881 cm to the nearest 100 cm
    (c) 32 499 g to the nearest 1000 g
    (d) 49 153 g to the nearest 10 kg

18. Round off the following measurements in cm to the nearest cm.
    (a) 4.45
    (b) 23.67
    (c) 107.05
    (d) 654.59

19. Round off the following measurements in kg to the nearest 0.1 kg.
    (a) 14.045
    (b) 57.496
    (c) 108.356
    (d) 763.247

20. Round off the following measurements in cm^2 to the nearest $\frac{1}{10}$ cm^2.
    (a) 7.0283
    (b) 40.08
    (c) 148.30
    (d) 168.353

Express the following numbers correct to the number of significant figures indicated within the brackets.

21. 4.0672   (2)   22. 0.076 952   (3)

23. 5003.583   (4)   24. 19.648 51   (2)

25. 18.08   (3)   26. 3.9054   (3)

27. 37.87   (2)   28. 18.1356   (4)

29. 0.008 165 4   (3)   30. 240.0489   (4)

31. 0.054 45   (2)   32. 0.032 56   (3)

33. Estimate the value of each of the following. Give your answer correct to one significant figure.

    (a) 4987×91.2
    (b) 0.0079×21.7
    (c) $\dfrac{8.98}{3.03}$

    (d) $\dfrac{163.4}{0.0818}$
    (e) $(398)^2 \times 0.062$

Estimate, correct to one significant figure, the value of the following.

34. $\dfrac{29.12 \times 5.167}{1.895}$

35. $\dfrac{41.41}{10.02 \times 0.018\ 65}$

36. $\dfrac{4.9 \times 57 \times 0.389}{20.128}$

37. $\dfrac{0.281 \times 0.007\ 24}{10.138 \times 0.0976}$

38. $\dfrac{\sqrt{24.977} \times 28.0349}{19.897}$

39. The Stevens are going on a 1097-km trip. They would like to drive half of the way on Monday and stay overnight at a hotel. Approximately how many kilometres should they drive on Monday before they stop at a hotel?

40. Mr Teh has 148 pencils and needs to sell them by the dozen. How many dozens can he sell?

41. Mary bought a dress that had an original price of $98.99 but it was marked 25% off because of a sale. About how much will the dress cost?

42. A happy meal costs $5.25 at Juwaida Chicken. Mr. Kentucky would like to buy 19 happy meals for a birthday party. About how much will the meals cost altogether?

43. John travelled 297 km on 19.91 litres of petrol. About how many km per litre of petrol does John's car get?

44. Raham would like to buy a rug for his living room. The lengths of the rug will be $4\frac{1}{12}$ m long and $2\frac{11}{12}$ wide. What is the approximate area of the rug that is needed for the living room?

45. Mr. Lim's annual salary is $47 899.52.
(a) What is his approximate monthly salary?
(b) In order to fill out his tax forms, Mr. Lim has to round off his salary to the nearest dollar. What should he write on the tax form for his salary?

46. There are 33 classrooms at Algebra Secondary School. If each classroom holds 37 students, approximately how many students can the school hold?

47. Alex wants to buy as many pens as he can. He has $8.15 and each pen costs 85 cents. How many pens can he buy?

48. Vikesh drives to work at 62 km per hour. His office is 22.5 km away. How long will it take Vikesh to get to his office?

49. The length and breadth of a rectangular sheet of metal are measured and recorded as 9.96 metres and 5.08 metres respectively. Estimate, correct to one significant figure,
(a) the perimeter in metres,
(b) the area, in square metres.

50. The length of the circumference of a circle is given by the formula $l = 2\pi r$ and its area given by the formula $A = \pi r^2$, where r is its radius. Find
(a) the approximate length of the circumference of a circle whose radius is
    (i) 497 mm,
    (ii) 5.12 m;
(b) the area of a circle whose radius is
    (i) 10.09 m,
    (ii) 98.4 mm.

Express the following numbers correct to one decimal place.

51.	34.29	**52.**	26.87	**53.**	138.08
54.	36.148	**55.**	2.497	**56.**	18.5095

Express the following numbers correct to two decimal places.

57.	4.698	**58.**	26.8047	**59.**	0.045
60.	14.937	**61.**	10.0968	**62.**	8.0994

Express the following numbers correct to three decimal places.

63. 0.037 64

64. 8.4453

65. 7.4495

66. 11.6387

67. 6.8282

68. 32.929 49

69. 13.450 93

70. 4.825 51

Express the following numbers correct to the number of decimal places shown in brackets.

71. 5.775 491 3   *(4)*

72. 0.088 259 1   *(2)*

73. 9.225 549 2   *(3)*

74. 0.0377   *(2)*

75. 37.129 36   *(3)*

76. 0.915 473 6   *(1)*

77. Evaluate $2 \times 3.42 \times (4.38 + 0.44)$, giving your answer **(i)** exactly, **(ii)** correct to two decimal places.

78. Express as a decimal, correct to three decimal places, the value of $(0.3)^3 - \dfrac{0.12}{6}$.

79. Find the value of 0.123×0.456, giving your answer **(i)** exactly, **(ii)** correct to four decimal places.

80. Evaluate $\dfrac{9.34 - 7.8}{0.4^2}$ **(i)** exactly, **(ii)** correct to one decimal place.

Use a calculator to evaluate each of the following, giving your answer correct to 3 decimal places.

81. $\dfrac{17.47 \times 6.87}{5.61 - 3.52}$

82. $\dfrac{6.52^2 \times 3.85^3}{100.3}$

83. $\dfrac{1.743 + 5.3}{11.71^2}$

84. $\dfrac{5.283 \times 16.49}{0.0359 \times 52.764}$

85. $\dfrac{119.73 - 13.27 \times 4.711}{88.77 \div 66.158}$

86. $7.593 - 6.219 \times \dfrac{1.47}{(1.4987)^3}$

87. $\left(\dfrac{32.41 - 10.479}{7.218}\right) \times \left(\dfrac{4.7103 \times 21.483}{8.4691}\right)$

88. How many articles can be bought with $7.67 if each article costs 59 cents?

89. Find the cost of 2.8 m of curtain material at $18.40 per metre.

90. The following purchases are made at a supermarket: 2.2 kg of tomatoes at $3.40 per kg, 1.2 kg of bananas at $1.50 per kg, 18 apples at 99¢ for 3 and 2 kg of potatoes at 81¢ per kg. How much will the total bill amount to?

91. A cash box contains 5-cent coins and 20-cent coins. Given that the total value of these coins is $7.35 and there are thirty-one 20-cent coins, find the number of 5-cent coins in the box.

Use your calculator to evaluate each of the following, giving your answer as **(a)** a fraction, **(b)** a decimal correct to 4 decimal places.

92. $\left(5\dfrac{5}{12} - 3\dfrac{17}{36}\right) \div 2\dfrac{1}{3} + \dfrac{2}{3} + 3\dfrac{1}{5}$

93. $7\dfrac{1}{5} \div \dfrac{18}{29} - \left(\dfrac{7}{16} + 2\dfrac{5}{12}\right) \times 2\dfrac{2}{11}$

94. $10 - \left(2\dfrac{9}{14} + \dfrac{11}{21}\right) \div 4\dfrac{3}{5} \times 10\dfrac{1}{6}$

95. $6\dfrac{1}{4} \times 8 - 3\dfrac{2}{3} \times 5\dfrac{1}{2} + 2\dfrac{2}{5} \times 4\dfrac{7}{12}$

96. $2\dfrac{1}{2} \times 48 - 3\dfrac{2}{3} \div \dfrac{1}{18} + 5\dfrac{5}{12} \div \dfrac{7}{36}$

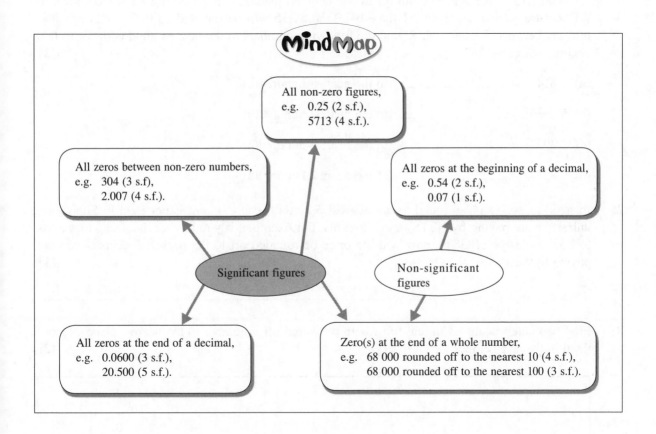

Real-life Mathematical Investigation: Rounding Up, Down or to the Nearest Place?

The purpose of this worksheet is to investigate when to round up, round down and to round off a number to the nearest place.

Section A: Rounding Off to the Nearest Place

1. In maths, we usually round off a number to the **nearest place**. For example, if we want to round 7.14 and 7.15 to the nearest tenth (or to one decimal place), then 7.14 will be rounded down to 7.1 because 7.14 is nearer to 7.1 than to 7.2. But 7.15 will be rounded up to 7.2 although it is midway between 7.1 and 7.2. Round the following numbers to the nearest hundredth (or to two decimal places). **[2]**

    (a) 1.614 = _____ (to the nearest hundredth)

    (b) 57.386 = _____ (to the nearest hundredth)

    (c) 2.3972 = _____ (to the nearest hundredth)

    (d) 0.8249 = _____ (to the nearest hundredth)

2. In real life, we can also round to the **nearest 5 cents** because 1 cent is not used in Singapore, unless we are paying by NETS or credit cards. For example, if you buy a school bag that costs $21.53 (inclusive of GST), how will the price be rounded off to the nearest 5 cents if you are paying by cash? **[1]**

    _____

3. Find two other examples in real life where we round off a number to the nearest place. Record them in the box below. **[2]**

Section B: Rounding Down

Scenario 1

4. In maths, when we round off to the nearest 5 cents, $7.14 will be rounded up to $7.15. In real life, most shops do so when you pay by cash for something that costs $7.14 (inclusive of GST). However, some shops actually **round $7.14 down to $7.10**! Why?   [2]

    _____

5. Find one example of these shops in Singapore that actually **round down** to the nearest 5 cents, instead of rounding off to the nearest 5 cents.   [1]

    _____

Scenario 2

6. Suppose you have $2 and you want to buy a few sweets that cost 30 cents each. What is the biggest number of sweets that you can buy?   [2]

    _____

7. In Q6, did you **round off** the number of sweets to the nearest whole number, or did you round **up** or round **down** the number? Why?   [2]

    _____

Scenario 3

8. Suppose you are the designer of a lift that can carry a maximum mass of 897 kg. You are told to put the maximum mass correct to the nearest 100 kg. What should you put the maximum mass as?   [1]

    _____

9. In Q8, did you **round off** the maximum mass to the nearest 100 kg? Did you round **up** or round **down** the number? Why?   [2]

    _____

Summary

10. In your own words, summarise the above three scenarios where it is more appropriate to **round down** a number than round it off to the nearest place.   [3]

    _____

    _____

    _____

New Syllabus Mathematics Workbook 1

11. Find two other examples in real life where we **round down** a number instead of rounding it off to the nearest place. Record them in the box below. [2]

```

```

Section C: Rounding Up

Scenario 1

12. In maths, when we round off to the nearest 5 cents, $5.57 will be rounded down to $5.55. In real life, most shops do so when you pay by cash for something that costs $5.57 (inclusive of 5% GST). However, some shops actually **round $5.57 up to $5.60**! Why? [1]

_____

Scenario 2

13. Suppose 212 students and 8 teachers are going for an excursion by bus and each bus can only carry 30 passengers. How many buses are required? [2]

_____

14. In Q13, did you **round off** the number of buses to the nearest whole number? Did you round **up** or round **down** the number? Why? [2]

_____

Summary

15. In your own words, summarise the above two scenarios where **rounding up** a number is more appropriate than rounding it off to the nearest place.   [2]

_____

_____

16. Find two other examples in real life where we **round up** a number instead of rounding it off to the nearest place. Record them in the box below.   [2]

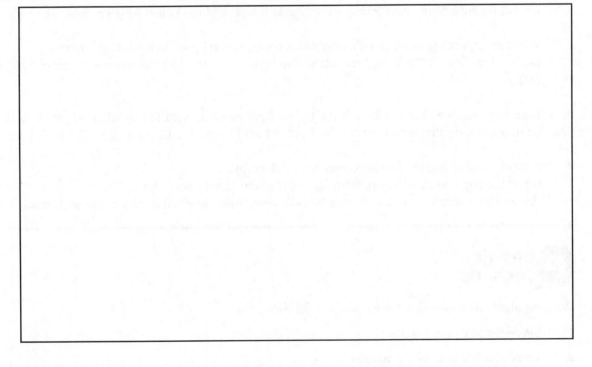

Conclusion

17. Write down one main lesson that you have learnt from this worksheet.   [1]

_____

Final Score:

☐ / 30

Final Score	24–30	20–23	15–19	10–14	0–9
Grade	A	B	C	D	F

Teacher's Comments (if any):

_____

_____

Chapter 5 Fundamental Algebra

1. In algebra, we use symbols, e.g. a, x^2 and xy, to represent numbers and variables. We add or subtract the like terms by adding or subtracting the coefficients, e.g. $2a + 5a = 7a$ and $7b - 3b = 4b$. We do not add the coefficients of unlike terms, so adding $3x$ and $4y$ gives $3x + 4y$.

2. When an expression of arithmetic operations contains brackets, work with the expressions within the brackets first. (If there are brackets within brackets, work with the innermost pair of brackets first.)

3. If an expression within brackets is multiplied by a number, each term within the brackets must be multiplied by that number when the brackets are removed, e.g. $2(a + 3b) = 2a + 6b$.

4. Factorisation of algebraic expressions can be done by
   (a) extracting common factors from all terms of the given expressions,
   (b) grouping terms in such a manner that the new terms obtained have a common factor.

Write an algebraic expression for each of the following.

1. Seven times x plus 3 times y.

2. Three x cubed plus two y squares.

3. Twice x^2 minus 4 times the cube root of y.

4. The cost of y apples which are sold at 3 for a dollar.

5. Nine times the product of x and $3h$ minus the quotient when k is divided by $2y$.

6. The cube of the sum of x and y minus the square root of the sum of $5x$ and $3y$.

If $a = 3$, $b = 2$ and $c = -1$, find the value of each of the following.

7. $a^3 + b^3 + c^3 - 2abc$

8. $(2a + b - c)(4b - 3c)$

9. $(a - b)^2 - (b - c)^2$

10. $\dfrac{a + 1}{2} - \dfrac{b + c}{4} + \dfrac{c - a}{3}$

11. $a^b - c^a + b^a$

12. $2a - 3b^2 + 3abc^2$

13. $\dfrac{a + b}{c} - \dfrac{ab - c}{b}$

14. $\dfrac{a^2 - b^2}{c^2} - \dfrac{a^3 - c}{c - 3b}$

15. Find the value of $x^3 + 2xy^2 + y^3$ when $x = 2$ and $y = -1$.

16. Find the value of $\dfrac{x+1}{x-1} + \dfrac{2x-1}{2x+1}$ when $x = -2$.

17. Find the value of $(2x - 1)(2x + 1)(2x + 3)$ when $x = -3$.

Simplify the following expressions.

18. $5a + 3a - 6a$

19. $3a - (5a - 4a)$

20. $3a + 4b - a - b$

21. $12a + 5b - 7a - 14b - 9a$

22. $5x + 7y + 3z - 2x - 4y + z$

23. $2p - 5q + 7r - 4p + 2q - 3r$

24. $12xy - 13xz + 5yz - 4xz$

25. $7abc - 4bca + 6cba - cba$

26. $3a^2 - 4a + 5a^2 - 7a + 4$

27. $2x^3 - 5x^2 + 7x^3 - 4x^2 + 5x$

28. $5ab - 1\dfrac{1}{2}\,ab + \dfrac{3}{4}\,bc + \dfrac{1}{4}\,cb$

Simplify each of the following.

29. $3(x - 2y) - 2(3x - y) + 6(x - y)$

30. $2(3x + y) - 5[3(x - 3y) - 4(2x - y)]$

31. $2x - 3\{2(5x - y) - 4[x - (7x - y)]\}$

32. $5p + 3q - 4r - (6q - 3p + r)$

33. $5a + 4b - 3c + \left(3\dfrac{1}{2}a + 2\dfrac{1}{2}b - 3\dfrac{1}{2}c\right) - \left(2a - 1\dfrac{1}{2}b + 1\dfrac{1}{2}c\right)$

34. $a(5a^2 - 4a - 3) - a^2(4a - 1) + a(1 - 2a^2)$

Simplify each of the following.

35. $\dfrac{4}{3a^2b} \div \dfrac{2}{9ab^2}$

36. $\dfrac{5}{6}x^2 \div \dfrac{3}{4}x$

37. $14x^6 \div 2x^3$

38. $\left(\dfrac{2xy}{z}\right)^2 \div \sqrt{\dfrac{9x^4y^6}{z^8}} \div \left(\dfrac{4x}{3z}\right)^3$

39. $\dfrac{2xy}{3z} \times \dfrac{5xz}{4y} \div \dfrac{15x^2y}{8yz}$

40. $\sqrt{\dfrac{9x^2}{36y^4}} \div \dfrac{2y}{9x^2}$

41. $\left(\dfrac{3xy}{z}\right)^2 \div \dfrac{2x^3y}{5z} \times \left(\dfrac{4x}{15y}\right)^2$

Simplify the following algebraic fractions.

42. $\dfrac{x}{2} + \dfrac{x-3}{3} - \dfrac{x-4}{4}$

43. $\dfrac{x+y}{2} - \dfrac{x+5y}{4} + \dfrac{5x-4y}{8}$

44. $\dfrac{2x-3y}{5} - \dfrac{x-6y}{10} + \dfrac{5x+6y}{15}$

45. $\dfrac{5x-6y}{7} + \dfrac{3x-4y}{14} - \dfrac{7x+9y}{21}$

Find the sum of the following expressions.

46. $a + b + c, 2b - c, 3c + a$

47. $a^2 + b^2 - c^2, 2c^2 - b^2 + a^2, 5a^2 + 7c^2$

48. $2ab + 3bc, 5ac - 5ba, 2cb + 5ab$

49. $5abc - 7cb + 4ac, 4cba - 4bc + 3ca$

50. $\frac{1}{2}xy, \frac{1}{3}xy^2 - \frac{1}{4}yx, \frac{1}{6}xy^2 + xy$

Subtract

51. $2x^3 + 5x^2 - 4x + 3$ from $7x^2 + 5x^3 - 4x - 5$.

52. $4x^2 + 7x^3 - 5x$ from $3x(2x^3 - 2x^2 + 7)$.

53. $12x^3 + 5x - 9$ from $2x(3x^2 - 5)$.

54. $2a(3a^2 - 5a) + 5$ from $6a(2 - 3a + 5a^2) - 4(a^2 + 5)$.

55. Subtract $2x^2 + 3x^3 - 5$ from the sum of $(2x^3 - 5x + 7)$ and $(2x - 5x^3 + 4)$.

56. Subtract the sum of $(2x^2 - 7x + 4)$ and $(5x - 4x^3 + 7)$ from the sum of $(3x^2 - 8x + 9)$ and $(15 - 4x - 3x^3)$.

Factorise each of the following.

57. $y(x + 3) + 2(x + 3)$

58. $3x(y - 2) - 4(y - 2)$

59. $3x(2y - 3) - 2(2y - 3)$

60. $2x(3x - y) - 5(3x - y)$

61. $3x(p + 5q) - 5(5q + p)$

62. $4h(3p + 2q) - 8(2q + 3p)$

63. $2h(3x + 2) - 6k(3x + 2)$

64. $(x + y)(p - 2q) + (x - y)(p - 2q)$

65. $(3x - y)(3h + 4k) - (x - y)(3h + 4k)$

66. $5x(3p + 2q - r) - 10y(3p + 2q - r)$

Factorise each of the following. Where there are no factors, state so.

67. $xy + 2y + 10 + 5x$

68. $3ax - ay + 6bx - 2by$

69. $15px - 10qx + 2qy - 3py$

70. $3hx + 7hy - 6kx - 14ky$

71. $3qy - 3py + 2px - 2qx$

72. $8hv - 9ku - 12kv + 6hu$

Exploratory Worksheet: Expansion of Algebraic Expressions

How do you *expand* $a(b + c)$? Or what is $a(b + c)$ equal to? For example, what is $4(2 + 3)$ equal to?

Section A: Exploration

Complete the table below. [2]

a	b	c	$a(b + c)$	ab	ac
4	2	3	$4(2 + 3) = 4 \times 5 = 20$	8	
7	1	4			
3	5	−2			
2	−3	5			
−2	3	4			
−1	6	2			

Section B: Findings

1. What do you notice about the numbers in the last 3 columns? [1]

    _____

2. To conclude, $a(b + c) =$ _____ [1]
    This is called the ***distributive law***.

3. With the help of a diagram, can you explain why it works for $4(2 + 3)$? Why is $4(2 + 3)$ not equal to $4 \times 2 + 3$? [3]

    Hint: Consider 4 groups of $2 + 3$. The first group of $2 + 3$ has been drawn for you below.

$$\underbrace{2}_{\bullet \quad \bullet} + \underbrace{3}_{\times \quad \times \quad \times}$$

Section C: Practice

4. Expand the following algebraic expressions. [3]

    (a) $2(x + y)$ =

    (b) $x(y + z)$ =

    (c) $k(p + q)$ =

    (d) $3c(a + b)$ =

    (e) $7(2x + y)$ =

    (f) $4p(x + 3t)$ =

    (g) $h(ac + b)$ =

    (h) $2k(p + qt)$ =

    (i) $ab(st + 3r)$ =

Final Score:

[ ] / 10

Final Score	8–10	7	5–6	4	0–3
Grade	A	B	C	D	F

Teacher's Comments (if any):

_____

_____

Term I Revision Test Time: $1\frac{1}{2}$ hours

Do not use calculators unless stated otherwise.

1. Find the difference between

   (a) $8^2 + \left(17\frac{1}{4}\right)^2$ and $\left(8 + 17\frac{1}{4}\right)^2$,

   (b) $\left(8 + 3\frac{1}{2}\right)^3$ and $8^3 + \left(3\frac{1}{2}\right)^3$. **[4]**

2. **(a)** Express the following fractions as decimals.

   (i) $\dfrac{13}{40}$ **(ii)** $\dfrac{25}{16}$ **[2]**

   (b) Express each of the following decimals as a fraction in its lowest terms.
   (i) 0.098 **(ii)** 1.0625 **[2]**

3. Express
   (a) 8.4454 correct to two decimal places,
   (b) 0.070 49 correct to two significant figures,
   (c) 25 958 correct to the nearest 100,
   (d) 15 997 correct to the nearest 10. **[4]**

4. **(a)** Express **(i)** 576, **(ii)** 5832 as a product of prime factors and write down the value of $\sqrt{576}$ and of $\sqrt[3]{5832}$. **[4]**
   (b) Find the H.C.F. of
   (i) 56, 84, **(ii)** 36, 54, 63. **[4]**
   (c) Find the L.C.M. of
   (i) 48, 120, **(ii)** 63, 105, 420. **[4]**

5. Evaluate
   (a) $\dfrac{(-24) + (-30)}{(-6)}$,

   (b) $(-2)^3 \times (-5) - 4 \times (-5)^2 - (-7)^2$,

   (c) $\dfrac{\left(\frac{1}{5} + \frac{1}{4}\right) \div \left(-\frac{1}{20}\right)}{\left(-1\frac{2}{5}\right) \times \left(-1\frac{1}{4}\right)}$,

   (d) $\dfrac{75 \times \left(-\frac{1}{2}\right) \times (-13.4)}{(0.5) \times 7.5}$. **[4]**

6. Use a calculator to evaluate each of the following and give your answers correct to two decimal places.
   (a) $79.12^2 + 56.19^2 - 2 \times 79.12 \times 56.19 \times 0.8716$

   (b) $\sqrt{\dfrac{121.56^2 + 78.94^2 - 99.18^2}{2 \times 121.56 \times 78.94}}$

   (c) $\dfrac{245 \times \sqrt[3]{269.78} + 996 \times \sqrt{294.81}}{4 \times (54.783)^3}$

   (d) $\sqrt[3]{29.76^3 + (8.567 - 0.914)^2}$ **[4]**

7. Factorise each of the following.
   (a) $5x + 15y$
   (b) $cx - 3dx + 2cy - 6dy$ **[3]**

8. Simplify
   (a) $3a - (2 - 5a) - 7$,
   (b) $8x - 3(x - y)$,
   (c) $4(3x - 7) - 2(6x - 7)$. **[3]**

9. Copy and complete the following.
   (a) $x - 2y + z = x - \boxed{}$
   (b) $2s + 5t - u + 3v = 2s + \boxed{}$

   (c) $\dfrac{x}{y} = \dfrac{\boxed{}}{py}$

   (d) $\dfrac{a}{2b} = \dfrac{ma}{\boxed{}}$

   (e) $\dfrac{\boxed{}}{6xy} = \dfrac{2pq}{3x}$ **[5]**

10. Estimate each of the following, giving your answer correct to one significant figure:
    (a) The number of books at $3.95 each that can be bought with a $100 note.
    (b) The number of litres of petrol for a 600-km journey by car if the consumption of petrol of the car is 12.1 km per litre.
    (c) $\sqrt[3]{7.95} \times 25.04$. **[3]**

11. If $a = 3$, $b = -2$ and $c = 5$, find the value of
    (a) $a + b + c$,
    (b) abc,
    (c) $\dfrac{1}{a} - \dfrac{1}{b} + \dfrac{1}{c}$.   **[4]**

12. Express the following in standard form:
    (a) 645 000,
    (b) 0.000 95,
    (c) $(8.6 \times 10^4) \times (4.0 \times 10^3)$,
    (d) $(5.84 \times 10^3) \div (8.0 \times 10^6)$.   **[4]**

13. (a) Find the size of each interior angle of a regular polygon with 24 sides.
    (b) If one interior angle of an octagon is 86° while the remaining interior angles are equal in size, find the size of one of these interior angles.
    (c) If the interior angles of a hexagon are in the ratio $3 : 3 : 3 : 3 : 4 : 4$, find the largest exterior angle.   **[6]**

Chapter 6 Number Sequences

Summary

1. A **number sequence** is a set of numbers arranged in such a way that each successive number follows the preceding one according to a specific rule. The numbers in a sequence are known as the **terms** of the sequence.

2. Some heuristics for problem solving are:
   - change your point of view
   - make an organised list
   - work backwards
   - make a supposition
   - use trial-and-error
   - think of a related problem
   - simplify the problem
   - eliminate the unlikely possibilities

   - draw a diagram
   - look for a pattern
   - write an equation
   - solve a simpler problem
   - solve part of the problem
   - use a table
   - use a model
   - act it out

Write down the next three terms in the following sequences:

1. 10, 100, 1000, ...
2. 1, 2, 6, 24, ...
3. 6, 11, 16, 21, ...
4. 2, 10, 50, ...
5. 1, 8, 27, 64, ...
6. 52, 47, 42, 37, ...
7. 2, 3, 5, 8, 12, ...
8. 21, 23, 26, 30, ...
9. 4, 5, 9, 18, 34, ...
10. 1024, 512, 256, 128, 64, ...
11. 7, 8, 10, 14, 22, ...
12. 90, 10, 80, 20, 70, 30, ...

Fill in the missing terms in the following sequences:

13. 0, 6, 12, 18, _____, _____
14. 11, 13, 16, 20, _____, _____
15. 156 250, 31 250, 6250, 1250, _____, _____
16. 47, 38, 30, _____, _____, 12, 8, 5
17. 25, _____, 26, 23, 27, 22
18. 2, 1, 3, 2, 4, _____, 5

19. Consider the pattern:

$$1 = 1^1$$
$$1 + 3 = 2^2$$
$$1 + 3 + 5 = 3^2$$
$$1 + 3 + 5 + 7 = 4^2$$
$$\vdots$$
$$1 + 3 + 5 + \ldots + (2k - 1) = 144$$
$$\vdots$$

   (a) Write down the eighth line in the pattern.
   (b) Find the value of k.

20. **(a)** Given the sequence 1, 3, 6, 10, 15, ..., write down the next four terms of the sequence. Similarly, write down the next four terms of the sequence 0, 1, 4, 10, 20, 35, ...
   (b) Consider

$$1^3 - 1 = 0 \quad = 6 \times 0$$
$$2^3 - 2 = 6 \quad = 6 \times 1$$
$$3^3 - 3 = 24 \quad = 6 \times 4$$
$$4^3 - 4 = 60 \quad = 6 \times 10$$
$$5^3 - 5 = 120 \quad = 6 \times 20$$
$$6^3 - 6 = 210 \quad = 6 \times 35$$
$$\vdots$$
$$m^3 - m = n \quad = k \times 84$$
$$\vdots$$

   Using the results in **(a)**,
   (i) write down the ninth and tenth lines in the pattern,
   (ii) find the value of m and of n.

21. **(a)** Given the sequence, 1, 1, 2, 3, 5, 8, 13, ..., write down the next five terms of the sequence.
   (b) Consider the pattern:

$$1^2 + 1^2 = 1 \times 2$$
$$1^2 + 1^2 + 2^2 = 2 \times 3$$
$$1^2 + 1^2 + 2^2 + 3^2 = 3 \times 5$$
$$1^2 + 1^2 + 2^2 + 3^2 + 5^2 = 5 \times 8$$
$$1^2 + 1^2 + 2^2 + 3^2 + 5^2 + 8^2 = 8 \times 13$$

   (i) Verify the result of the 5th line.
   (ii) Using the result in **(a)**, write down the next four lines in the pattern.
   (iii) Describe how the terms in the sequence in **(a)** are connected in the pattern.

22.

110	209								
121									
								979	
								891	990

(a) Complete the above table with the three-digit multiples of 11, column by column from top to bottom.

(b) Describe as many patterns as you can see from the table.

(c) There are two multiples in the table such that when each is divided by 11, the resulting quotient is equal to the sum of the squares of the digits. Find these two multiples.

23. Judith designs a sequence of patterns consisting of circles and squares joined by straight lines. The first three patterns she designs are shown below.

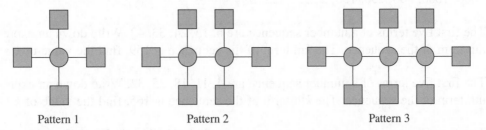

Pattern 1   Pattern 2   Pattern 3

(a) Draw the next two patterns and complete the table below.

No. of circles	1	2	3	4	5	...	n
No. of squares	$2 \times (1 + 1) = 4$	$2 \times (2 + 1) = 6$	$2 \times (3 + 1) = 8$			...	$2 \times (n + 1)$
No. of straight lines	$3 \times 1 + 1$	$3 \times 2 + 1$	$3 \times 3 + 1$			...	

(b) How many circles, squares and straight lines are there in the
   (i) 10th pattern,   (ii) 105th pattern?

(c) Find the number of circles and the number of straight lines in a pattern which has 30 squares.

24. Raymond draws different sets of points in a plane, no three of which are lying on a straight line. The first four sets of points are shown below.

1 point	2 points	3 points	4 points

Set 1   Set 2   Set 3   Set 4

When any two points are joined, a line segment is formed.
(a) Draw the next two sets of points and complete the table below.

No. of points	1	2	3	4	5	...	n
No. of line segments formed	$\dfrac{1 \times (1-1)}{2} = 0$	$\dfrac{2 \times (2-1)}{2} = 1$	$\dfrac{3 \times (3-1)}{2} = 3$			...	$\dfrac{n \times (n-1)}{2}$

(b) How many line segments can be formed in the pattern with
   (i) 16 points   **(ii)** 24 points?
(c) How many such points are needed to form 190 line segments?

Write down the next two terms in each of the following number sequences. Hence, or otherwise, write down an expression for the nth term of the sequence.

25. 12, 17, 22, 27, 32, _____, _____

26. 83, 77, 71, 65, 59, _____, _____

27. 2, 9, 16, 23, 30, _____, _____

28. 1, 2, 4, 8, 16, _____, _____

29. 2, 6, 18, 54, 162, _____, _____

30. 12, 36, 108, 324, 972, _____, _____

31. 7, 13, 19, 25, 31, _____, _____

32. 39, 35, 31, 27, 23, _____, _____

33. 2000, 1000, 500, 250, 125, _____, _____

34. The first five terms of a number sequence are 6, 15, 24, 33, 42. Write down an expression for the nth term of the sequence. The kth term of the sequence is 159, find the value of k.

35. The first five terms of a number sequence are 4, 11, 18, 25, 32. Write down an expression for the nth term of the sequence. The kth term of the sequence is 165, find the value of k.

36. The first five terms of a number sequence are 3, 6, 12, 24, 48. Write down, in terms of n, an expression for the nth term of the sequence. If the rth term of the sequence is 1536, find the value of r.

37. The first five terms of a number sequence are 747, 726, 705, 684, 663. Write down, in terms of n, an expression for the nth term of the sequence. If the kth term of the sequence is 390, find the value of k.

38. The first five terms of a number sequence are 1024, 512, 256, 128, 64. Write down, in terms of n, an expression for the nth term of the sequence. If the hth term of the sequence is $\dfrac{1}{4}$, find the value of h.

Real-life Mathematical Investigation: Mathematics, Rabbits & Flowers

The purpose of this worksheet is to investigate how mathematics is involved in the birth rates of rabbits and the petals of flowers.

Section A: Rabbits

1. A man bought a pair of rabbits (one male and one female) in Jan 2006. The rabbits did not produce any rabbits in Feb 2006 but they produced a new pair of rabbits (one male and one female) every month from Mar 2006 onwards. Each new pair of rabbits followed the same behaviour. For example, the pair of rabbits born in Mar 2006 did not produce any rabbits in Apr 2006 but they produced a new pair of rabbits every month from May 2006 onwards.

   (a) How many new pairs of rabbits were produced at the end of Mar 2006?

   Answer: _____ [1]

   (b) How many new pairs of rabbits were produced at the end of Apr 2006?

   Answer: _____ [1]

   (c) Draw a model in the table below to show the number of new pairs of rabbits produced at the end of each month from Jan to Sep 2006. Some parts have been done for you. Complete the last two columns of the table also. **[2]**

   ◯ 1st pair of rabbits   ⊗ Pairs produced by 2nd pair

   ● Pairs produced by 1st pair   ⊕ Pairs produced by 3rd pair

   For other pairs produced, you can use the same symbol ◯.

Month	Model	Total **New Pairs** at End of Month	Total Pairs at End of Month
Jan		0	1
Feb		0	1
Mar		1	2
Apr		1	
May		2	
Jun			
Jul			
Aug			
Sep			

2. The last column in the table above shows the **total pairs** of rabbits at the end of each month. This number pattern is called the *Fibonacci sequence*. Explain how you get the next term. **[2]**

_____

3. How many pairs of rabbits were there at the end of Jan 2007? **Answer:** _____ **[1]**

Section B: Flowers

4. Write down the number of petals[1] for each flower in the space beside the name. **[1]**

Picture A: White Calla Lily _____   Picture B: Euphorbia _____
(Note: There are 4 flowers in the picture.)

---

[1] For botanists, some of these so-called 'petals' are actually sepals or bracts, but we would not differentiate between them here.

Picture C: Waterplantain _____

Picture D: White Vinca _____

Picture E: Moonbeam Coreopsis _____

Picture F: Orange Zinnia _____

5. What do you notice about these numbers? [1]

_____

6. However, there are exceptions. Write down the number of petals for each flower in the space beside the name. [1]

Picture G: Ixora _____

Picture H: Daylily _____

Picture I: Starflower _____   Picture J: Passion Flower _____

7. One type of exception is that the number of petals follows the Lucas Sequence. The Lucas Sequence is just like the Fibonacci Sequence except that the starting two numbers are 2 and 1, instead of 1 and 1. Write down the next 5 terms in the Lucas Sequence below: **[1]**

    2, 1, 3, _____ , _____ , _____ , _____ , _____ , ...

8. State the first 3 numbers in the Lucas Sequence that are **not** Fibonacci numbers.   **[1]**

    _____

9. Compare your answers in Q6 and Q8. Which flowers are still exceptions, i.e. their number of petals is **not** a Fibonacci or a Lucas number? Write down their number of petals also.   **[1]**

    _____

10. The second type of exception is that the number of petals follows a sequence like the Fibonacci Sequence except that the starting two numbers are 2 and 2. Write down the next 5 terms of this sequence below: **[1]**

    2, 2, 4, _____ , _____ , _____ , _____ , _____ , ...

11. Compare your answers in Q9 and Q10. Which flowers are still exceptions?   **[1]**

    _____

12. The third type of exception is mutants or hybrids created artificially. Nowadays, roses come with many different petals because they have been created artificially. Search the Internet to find how many petals a wild rose (i.e. **not** a hybrid) has. **Hint:** It is a Fibonacci number.   **[1]**

    _____

13. Hence write down the number of petals a natural flower (excluding mutants) can have. Just list the first 10 numbers.   **[1]**

    _____

Further Investigation

14. One of the most important questions in any mathematical investigation that you should ask yourself is: *"What else is there for me to investigate?"* List one thing related to this topic that you would like to investigate further and investigate it. [2]

Question: _____

Answer:

Conclusion

15. Write down one main lesson that you have learnt from this worksheet. [1]

_____

Final Score:

[   ] / 20

Final Score	16–20	13–15	10–12	7–9	0–6
Grade	A	B	C	D	F

Teacher's Comments (if any):

_____

_____

Fibonacci Sequence

This worksheet should be done after you have attempted the *Real-life Mathematical Investigation on Mathematics, Rabbits and Flowers* on page 47.

Section A: More Fibonacci Patterns in Nature

1. What other patterns in nature have something to do with the Fibonacci sequence?
    Visit the appropriate website (see Preface) and write a summary in **your own words**. You may draw pictures to illustrate.   [4]

Section B: Using Excel to Generate Fibonacci Numbers

How do you generate a list of Fibonacci numbers using Microsoft Excel? Excel is free as most computers are installed with Microsoft Office. Alternatively, use another free spreadsheet.

(a) Open an Excel Workbook.

(b) Enter in Cell A3: n

(c) Enter in Cell A4: 1

(d) Enter in Cell A5: 2

(e) Select both Cells A4 and A5.

(f) Point the cursor at the bottom right hand corner of the selection and the cursor will turn into a black cross.

(g) Click and drag to Cell A28. This will auto-complete Cells A6 to A28 with numbers 3, 4, 5, …, 25.

(h) Enter in Cell B3: Tn

(i) Select n in Cell B3. Choose from Toolbar: *Format* ▶ *Cells*… Then choose Font ▶ *Subscript* and click *OK*. The end result in Cell B3 is: T_n.

(j) Enter in Cell B4: 1

(k) Enter in Cell B5: 1

(l) Enter in Cell B6: =B4 + B5   [This is a formula.]

(m) Select the Cell B6. Repeat (f) and (g) to auto-complete until Cell B28. The end result is a list of Fibonacci numbers:

	A	B	C
1		Fibonacci Sequence	
2			
3	n	T_n	
4	1	1	
5	2	1	
6	3	2	
7	4	3	
8	5	5	
9	6	8	

Microsoft Excel - MI_Fibonacci.xls

File Edit View Insert Format Tool

B6   fx =B4+B5

2. What is the 25th Fibonacci number?   **[1]**

_____

3. Select Cell B7. Look for its formula in the Toolbar *fx*. State the formula.   **[1]**
=

_____

4. Explain how the formula in Cell B7 works.   **[1]**

_____

Section C: Using Excel to Generate Golden Ratio

The ratio T_n / T_{n-1} is a sequence that will converge to a limit. In the same Excel Workbook, we will construct this sequence.

(n) Enter in Cell C3: T_n / T_{n-1} [Format the subscripts as in (i)]

(o) Enter in Cell C5: =B5/B4

(p) Select the Cell C5. Repeat (f) and (g) to auto-complete until Cell C28. The end result is a sequence that converges to a limit:

	Microsoft Excel - MI_Fibonacci.xls [Read-Only

	File	Edit	View	Insert	Format	Tools	Data

| C6 | | | f_x =B6/B5 |

	A	B	C	D
1		Fibonacci Sequence		
2				
3	n	T_n	T_n / T_{n-1}	
4	1	1		
5	2	1	1	
6	3	2	2	
7	4	3	1.5	
8	5	5	1.666666667	
9	6	8	1.6	

5. Write down this limit, correct to 5 decimal places.   **[1]**

6. This limit in Q5 is called the ***Golden Ratio*** ϕ (pronounced as 'phi'). Use a calculator to evaluate $\dfrac{1 + \sqrt{5}}{2}$ and write down its value, correct to 5 decimal places. What do you notice?   **[1]**

7. Use a calculator to evaluate ϕ^2 and write down its value, correct to 5 decimal places. What do you notice? How is ϕ^2 related to ϕ (other than squaring ϕ)?   **[1]**

8. Use a calculator to evaluate $\dfrac{1}{\phi}$ and write down its value, correct to 5 decimal places. What do you notice? How is $\dfrac{1}{\phi}$ related to ϕ (other than taking the reciprocal of ϕ)?   **[1]**

9. Search the Internet to find out more about the history and significance of the Golden Ratio. Write a summary in **your own words**. You may draw pictures to illustrate, if any. [3]

Conclusion

10. Write down one main lesson that you have learnt from this worksheet. [1]

_____

Final Score:

☐ / 15

Final Score	12–15	10–11	8–9	6–7	0–5
Grade	A	B	C	D	F

Teacher's Comments (if any):

_____

_____

Chapter 7 Algebraic Equations and Simple Inequalities

1. To solve an equation, we can
   (a) add the same number to each side;

   e.g. if $x - 5 = 7,$
   then $(x - 5) + 5 = 7 + 5$

   (b) subtract the same number from each side;

   e.g. if $x + 4 = 15$
   then $(x + 4) - 4 = 15 - 4$

   (c) multiply each side by the same number;

   e.g. if $\dfrac{1}{3}x = 8$

   then $3\left(\dfrac{1}{3}x\right) = 3(8)$

   (d) divide each side by the same number, except 0.

   e.g. if $3x = 21$

   then $\dfrac{3x}{3} = \dfrac{21}{3}$

2. To solve an inequality, we can multiply or divide both sides of an inequality by a positive number without having to change the inequality sign.

   If $x > y$, then $xa > ya$ and $\dfrac{x}{a} > \dfrac{y}{a}$ $(a > 0)$.

   If we multiply or divide both sides of an inequality by a negative number, we have to change the inequality sign.

   If $x > y$, then $xa < ya$ and $\dfrac{x}{a} < \dfrac{y}{a}$ $(a < 0)$.

Solve the following equations.

1. $2x - 7 = 3$	**2.** $5x + 2 = 7$	**3.** $15 - 2x = 9$
4. $17 + 3x = -3$	**5.** $7x - 14 = 18 - 4x$	**6.** $9x + 4 = 3x - 9$

Solve the following equations.

7. $\dfrac{3}{4}x = 15$

8. $\dfrac{2}{5}x - 1 = 4$

9. $\dfrac{x}{3} + 5 = 15$

10. $2 + \dfrac{5}{7}x = 1\dfrac{1}{4}$

11. $\dfrac{3x - 4}{5} - 7 = 0$

12. $\dfrac{2x - 1}{3} = 1 - x$

Solve the following equations.

13. $3(x - 4) = 7$

14. $5(2x + 3) = 35$

15. $7(x + 4) = 2(x - 4)$

16. $2(5 - 2x) = 4(2 - 3x)$

17. $\dfrac{1}{4}(5x + 4) = \dfrac{1}{3}(2x - 1)$

18. $2x - [3 + (x - 5)] = 6$

Solve the following equations.

19. $\dfrac{1}{3}(x - 3) - x + 5 = 3(x - 1)$

20. $\dfrac{2(x - 1)}{3} + \dfrac{3x}{4} = 0$

21. $\dfrac{6x + 1}{7} - \dfrac{2x - 7}{3} = 4$

22. $4x + 1 - \dfrac{1}{2}(3x - 2) - \dfrac{1}{3}(4x - 1) = 0$

23. $\dfrac{2x}{9} - \dfrac{x - 1}{6} = \dfrac{x + 3}{12}$

24. $\dfrac{3x - 4}{6} - \dfrac{2x + 3}{8} = \dfrac{2x - 7}{24}$

25. $\dfrac{2}{3}x + 3 = 2\dfrac{1}{2}x + 5$

26. $\dfrac{1}{2}\left(2x - \dfrac{1}{2}\right) = \dfrac{1}{3}\left(3x - \dfrac{1}{4}\right) + \dfrac{1}{4}(4x - 3)$

Solve the following equations. Give your answers correct to 2 decimal places where necessary.

27. $0.15x + 2.35(x - 2) = 1.3$

28. $\dfrac{x}{4} = \dfrac{x + 12}{10} + 0.6$

29. $\dfrac{5x + 2}{7} = \dfrac{x - 3}{5} + x + 1.5$

30. $0.5x + 2 = \dfrac{1}{4} + \dfrac{x - 1}{3} + \dfrac{1}{4}x - \dfrac{1}{6}$

Solve the following equations.

31. $\dfrac{3}{x} + \dfrac{4}{x} = 5$

32. $\dfrac{2}{x} - \dfrac{3}{x} + 1 = 3$

33. $\dfrac{5}{1 - x} + \dfrac{7}{2 - 2x} = 4$

34. $\dfrac{5}{x + 2} - \dfrac{3}{2x + 4} = 7$

Find the unknown value in each case.

35. If $xy - 3y^2 = 15$, find x when $y = 2$.

36. If $3u - 4uv = 5v^2$, find u when $v = 4$.

37. If $p - 5q = 4qr$, find p when $q = 4$ and $r = -1$.

38. If $x - y = \dfrac{xy}{p - q}$, find x when $y = 2$, $p = 5$ and $q = 6$.

39. If $\dfrac{x-1}{y+3} - \dfrac{x}{y} = \dfrac{1}{z}$, find x when $y = 8$ and $z = 2$.

40. If $\dfrac{2x+y-3z}{y+3x} = \dfrac{x}{2y}$, find x when $y = 4$ and $z = 1$.

41. If $A = P + \dfrac{PRT}{100}$,

    (a) find A when $P = 5000$, $R = 5$ and $T = 3$, **(b)** find P when $A = 6500$, $R = 5$ and $T = 1\dfrac{2}{3}$.

42. If $\dfrac{3x-5y}{7x-4y} = \dfrac{3}{4}$, find the value of $\dfrac{x}{y}$.

43. If $\dfrac{x-4y}{5x+y} = \dfrac{3}{5}$, find the value of $\dfrac{x}{3y}$.

44. A number exceeds another by 4 and their sum is 32. Find the two numbers.

45. When a number is doubled and 5 is subtracted from the result, the answer is 37. What is the number?

46. The sum of two numbers is 120. If the larger number is four times the smaller number, what are the two numbers?

47. The sum of three consecutive even numbers is 210. Find the largest of these numbers.

48. The sum of three consecutive odd numbers is 243. Find the three numbers.

49. The sum of five consecutive even numbers is 220. Find the smallest of these numbers.

50. Find two consecutive odd numbers such that when the smaller number is subtracted from three times the bigger number, the result is 56.

51. When a number is divided by 4 and has 12 subtracted from it, the result is $\dfrac{1}{6}$ of the number. What is the number?

52. Ahmad is twice as old as Bobby. John is 7 years younger than Ahmad. If the sum of their ages is 38, how old are the three boys?

53. A man was 26 years old when his son was born. Now, he is three times as old as his son. How old is the son now?

54. Ben is three times as old as Carl now. In two years' time, Ben will be twice as old as Carl. How old is Carl now?

55. Zhongmin is 50 years old. His son, Mingyong is 24 years old. How many years ago was Zhongmin three times as old as Mingyong?

56. Adam is 5 times as old as Charles. In 8 years' time, the sum of their ages will be equal to twice Adam's present age. Find their present ages.

57. A, B and C shared $1540. A received three times as much money as B and C's share is half that of A's. How much money did C receive?

58. A librarian bought 50 books for a library. Each hard cover book is $1\frac{1}{2}$ times as expensive as each paperback which costs $4 each. How many hard cover books did the librarian buy if he spent a total of $256 on the books?

59. Divide $240 among Aravin, Ben and Chandran such that Aravin will have twice as much money as Ben and Chandran will have one-quarter of what Aravin and Ben have altogether? How much money will Chandran receive?

60. Mary has 54 coins which are either 20-cent coins or 50-cent coins. If the total amount is $20.70, how many 20-cent coins does Mary have?

61. The length of a rectangle is 7 cm longer than its width. If the perimeter of the rectangle is 74 cm, find the length and the area of the rectangle.

62. Solve each of the following equations:

(a) $x = \dfrac{x + 8}{4}$ **(b)** $1 - \dfrac{2x}{5} = 4$ **(c)** $\dfrac{x}{3} - \dfrac{x}{5} = 4$

(d) $3x = \dfrac{9}{5}$ **(e)** $3x + 2 = x + 7$ **(f)** $x + 5 = 2 - 3(x - 4)$

(g) $5x - 7 = 17 - 3(2 - x)$

63. A hawker bought x kg of beef at $8.50 per kg and $(2x + 5)$ kg of chicken at $3.60 per kg. If the total cost was $206.40, find the value of x.

64. Peter and Jane together have $90. If Peter gave Jane $16, he would then have $14 less than Jane. How much does Peter originally have?

65. On a journey of 375 km, a motorist travels part of the journey on an expressway at 95 km/h and the rest at 65 km/h. The total time he spends on the stretch of road at 65 km/h is twice the time he spends on the expressway. How long did he take for the whole journey?

66. Solve the following inequalities.

(a) $3x > 33$ **(b)** $\dfrac{1}{2}x > 2.5$ **(c)** $0.4x < 3.2$

(d) $3x < -4.8$ **(e)** $3x + 2 < 8$ **(f)** $6x - 5 < -2$

67. For every 20 pupils going on a local school excursion, a teacher is needed to accompany them. How many teachers are needed to accompany a group of 154 pupils?

68. A mini bus can ferry a maximum of 28 pupils, how many mini buses will be needed to ferry a group of 184 pupils?

69. To photocopy mathematics and science worksheets for the class of 38, the treasurer of the class has to pay $43.20, how much must the treasurer collect from each pupil correct to the nearest ten cents?

70. The school's pocket money fund for the needy pupils collected a total of $4385. If this amount is to be given to a total of 32 needy pupils, how much can each needy pupil get, correct to the nearest $5?

Problem Posing: Linear Equations

You are given an equation like this:

$$5x - 2 = 33$$

Write a problem in the space below that will lead to the formation of the above equation and then solve the equation to answer your own problem. Let your creativity flow!

Note: Do **NOT** use *x* as part of your problem.

Scoring Rubric

Competency Level	Conceptual Understanding	Creativity	Mathematical Communication
4	• Showed complete understanding of velocity-time graph • Used appropriate mathematical terms	• Made up an interesting and original story	• Accurate solutions for questions posed
3	• Showed nearly complete understanding of velocity-time graph • Used nearly correct mathematical terms	• Made up an interesting story though not original	• Minor errors in solutions for questions posed
2	• Showed some understanding of velocity-time graph • Used many wrong mathematical terms	• Made up a simple or common story	• Some errors in solutions for questions posed
1	• Showed limited understanding of velocity-time graph • Misuse of or failure to use mathematical terms	• Made up a story with some errors	• Major errors in solutions for questions posed
0	• Showed no understanding of velocity-time graph • Failure to use mathematical terms	• Made up a totally irrelevant story	• Failure to provide solutions for questions posed
Score			

Final Score:

☐ / 12

Final Score	10–12	8–9	6–7	4–5	0–3
Grade	A	B	C	D	F

Teacher's Comments (if any):

_____

_____

Chapter 8 Perimeter and Area of Simple Geometrical Figures

 **Summary**

1. Area of a parallelogram = base × height

2. Area of trapezium = $\frac{1}{2}$ × height × sum of parallel sides

 **Practice Questions**

Find the perimeter of each of the following.

1. A square whose sides are
   (a) 6 cm,
   (b) 0.4 cm,
   (c) $\frac{3}{5}$ cm.

2. A square whose sides are
   (a) 5.4 cm,
   (b) 8.6 cm,
   (c) 78 mm.

3. A rectangle whose length and width are respectively
   (a) 7 cm, 6 cm,
   (b) 1.2 m, 80 cm,
   (c) 4.6 cm, 25 mm.

4. A rectangle whose length and width are repectively
   (a) 8 m, 6.4 m,
   (b) 2.35 m, 1.26 m,
   (c) $1\frac{3}{8}$ cm, $\frac{7}{8}$ cm.

Copy and complete each of the following.

5. $7.3 \text{ cm}^2 = \underline{\quad} \text{ mm}^2$

6. $4.65 \text{ m}^2 = \underline{\quad} \text{ cm}^2$

7. $0.054 \text{ ha} = \underline{\quad} \text{ m}^2$

8. $2.6 \text{ km}^2 = \underline{\quad} \text{ ha}$

9. $4650 \text{ mm}^2 = \underline{\quad} \text{ cm}^2$

10. $200\,000 \text{ cm}^2 = \underline{\quad} \text{ m}^2$

11. $50\,000 \text{ mm}^2 = \underline{\quad} \text{ m}^2$

12. $6\,500\,000 \text{ cm}^2 = \underline{\quad} \text{ ha}$

13. $0.0032 \text{ ha} = \underline{\quad} \text{ cm}^2$

14. Find the perimeter of each of the following squares if the area are
    (a) 64 cm^2,
    (ii) 0.25 m^2,
    (iii) 1.44 m^2.

Find the perimeter of each of the following rectangle of

15. area 48 cm^2 and length 8 cm.

16. area 0.9 m^2 and length 1.2 m.

17. area 1.76 cm^2 and width 8 mm.

18. Find the area of each of the following squares whose perimeters are
    (a) 84 cm,   (b) 0.8 cm,   (c) 1.24 m.

Find the area of each of the following.

19. A rectangle of length 14 cm and breadth 12 cm.

20. A rectangle of length 1.2 m and breadth 75 cm.

21. A parallelogram with base 6 cm and height 4.2 cm.

22. A parallelogram with base 4.6 m and height 2.5 m.

23. A triangle with base 2.4 cm and height 20 mm.

24. A trapezium of height 14 cm and parallel sides 8 cm and 12 cm.

25. A trapezium of height 1.2 m and parallel sides 45 cm and 75 cm.

For questions 26 and 28, take π to be 3.14.

26. Find the circumference of each of the following circles if its
    (a) radius is 10 cm,   (b) diameter is 60 cm,   (c) diameter is 1.2 m,
    (d) area is 50.24 cm^2,   (e) area is 452.16 cm^2,   (f) area is 2826 cm^2.

27. Find the area of each of the following circles, given that the
    (a) radius is 14 cm,   (b) radius is 4.2 cm,   (c) diameter is 56 cm,
    (d) diameter is 84 mm,   (e) circumference is 132 cm,

28. Find the diameter of each of the following circles if its
    (a) circumference is 78.5 cm,   (b) circumference is 125.6 m,
    (c) circumference is 244.92 mm,   (d) circumference is 0.471 m,
    (e) area is 78.5 cm^2.

Find the perimeter and area of each of the following blocks. All measures are in centimetres (cm).

29.

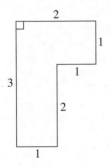

30.

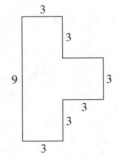

31.

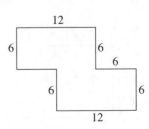

32.

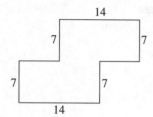

Find the areas of each of the following figures. All measurements are in centimetres (cm).

33.

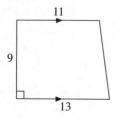

34.

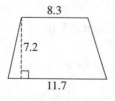

35.

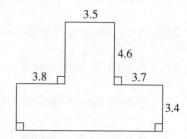

36.

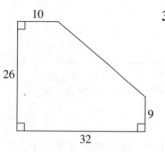

37.

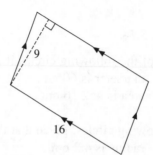

38.

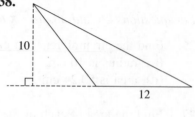

39.

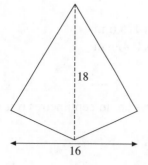

40.

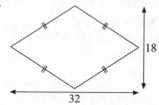

41.

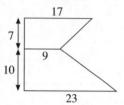

42.

Find the perimeter and area of each of the following figures where all the arcs shown are arcs of circles. All measurements are in centimetres (cm). Take $\pi = 3\frac{1}{7}$.

43.

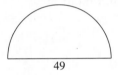

49

44.

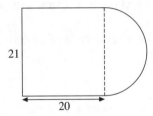

21

20

45.

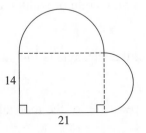

14

21

46.

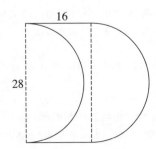

16

28

Find the area and perimeter of each of the shaded regions. Take $\pi = 3.14$ and give your answers correct to 3 significant figures. All measurements are in centimetres (cm).

47.

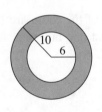

10

6

48.

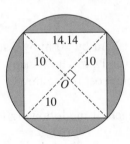

14.14

10

10

O

10

49.

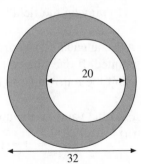

20

32

50.

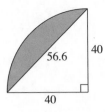

56.6

40

40

51.

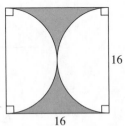

16

16

52.

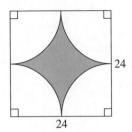

24

24

53.

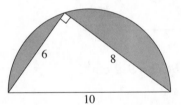

6

8

10

54.

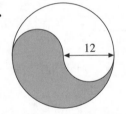

12

55. Two wire circles of diameters 28 cm and 35 cm are cut and then joined to form a big circle of radius k cm. Find the value of k.

56. The length of a rectangle is 7 times its width. If its perimeter is 120 cm, find its area.

57. The perimeter of a semicircle is 61.68 cm. Find
   (a) its dimater
   (ii) its area.
   (Take $\pi = 3.14$)

58. The perimeter of a quadrant of a circle is 71.4 cm. Find its area. (Take $\pi = 3.14$)

59. A photograph measuring 40 cm by 25 cm is framed up with a uniform margin of width 4 cm all around it. Find the area of the margin.

60. The length of a rectangle is three times its width. If the perimeter of the rectangle is 144 cm, find its area.

61. The length of a rectangular football field is twice its width. If the perimeter of the football field is 360 m, find its area, giving your answer in hectares.

62. A square field is 800 metres wide.
   (a) It is to be fenced up at a cost of \$3.50 per metre. How much will it cost?
   (b) It is to be sprayed with chemicals at a cost of 1.5 cents per square metre. What is the cost of spraying the field?

63. A rectangular classroom measures 12 cm by 10 m by 3 m. The four walls of the room are to be painted. If one litre of paint can cover 12 m^2, how many litres of paint must one buy in order to paint the four walls? What is the total cost if one litre of paint costs \$6.50?

64. Find the value of the unknown in each of the following figures.
   (a)

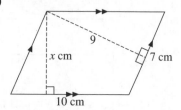

   (b)

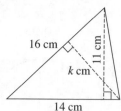

   (c)

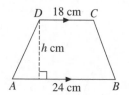

   Area of $ABCD = 273 \text{ cm}^2$

   (d)

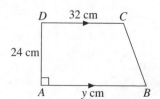

   Area of $ABCD = 912 \text{ cm}^2$

65.

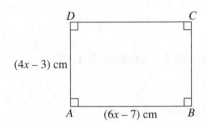 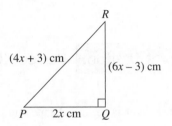

ABCD is a rectangle which measures $(6x - 7)$ cm by $(4x - 3)$ cm. *PQR* is a right angled triangle in which $PQ = 2x$ cm, $QR = (6x - 3)$ cm and $PR = (4x + 3)$ cm. If the perimeter of the rectangle is equal to the perimeter of the triangle, *PQR*, form an equation in *x* and solve it. What is the area of rectangle *ABCD* and triangle *PQR*? Do they have the same area?

66. Calculate the area of the shaded region given that the radius of the circle is 80 mm. (Take $\pi = 3.14$)

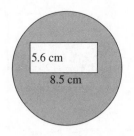

67. In the diagram, *CDE* is an isosceles triangle with an area of 24 cm². If $AB = 8$ cm and $AD = 12$ cm, calculate the area of the trapezium *ABED*.

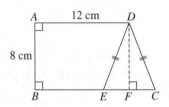

68. A quadrant of a circle of radius 10 cm is removed from a rectangle 15 cm wide and 24 cm long, as shown in the figure. Taking π to be 3.14, calculate the area and perimeter of the shaded region. Give your answers correct to 3 significant figures.

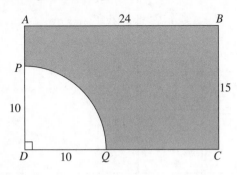

Mathematical Investigation: Perfect Rectangle and Golden Ratio

The purpose of this worksheet is to investigate the "beauty" of perfect rectangles.

Section A: Perfect Rectangle

1. Which one of the following rectangles do you like best? Your opinion may be different from your classmates' or friends'. **[no mark]**

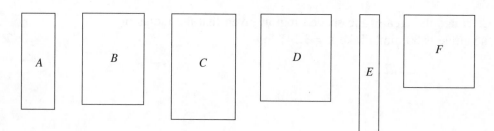

Your choice: _____

2. The diagram below shows a series of squares. The two smallest squares S_1 and S_2 have lengths of 1 unit each. Complete the table below. **[2]**

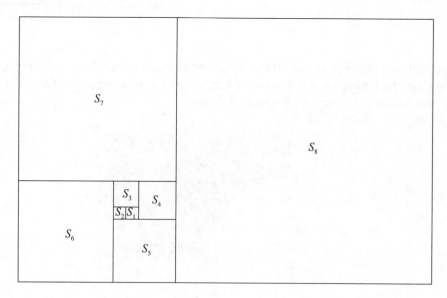

Square S_n	Length of Square L_n	$\dfrac{L_n}{L_{n-1}}$ (to 8 s.f.)
S_1	1	–
S_2	1	$\dfrac{1}{1} = 1$
S_3		
S_4		
S_5		
S_6		
S_7		
S_8		

3. What do you notice about the numbers in the middle column of the above table? **[1]**

_____

4. What is the significance of the ratio $\dfrac{L_8}{L_7}$? **[1]**

   Hint: Ratio of something for some rectangle in Q2. Use a pencil to highlight the rectangle in Q2. **[1]**

_____

5. Is the rectangle in Q4 about the same shape as Rectangle C in Q1? **[1]**

_____

6. Is Rectangle C your favourite rectangle in Q1? It is all right if your choice is different.
   [no mark]

_____

7. Rectangle C is called the ***Perfect Rectangle*** because it is supposed to be the most pleasing to the eyes for most people. Measure the length and the width of Rectangle C and calculate the ratio of its length to its width. **[1]**

_____

8. The ratio $\dfrac{L_n}{L_{n-1}}$ in the last column of the table in Q2 converges to the value 1.61803 39887...

This value is called the **Golden Ratio** ϕ (pronounced as 'phi'). Is this value about the same as your answer in Q7? What does this mean? **[1]**

_____

9. Use a calculator to evaluate $\dfrac{1+\sqrt{5}}{2}$ and write down its value. What do you notice? **[1]**

_____

Section B: Some Interesting Properties of the Golden Ratio

10. Use a calculator to evaluate ϕ^2 and write down its value, correct to 5 decimal places. What do you notice? How is ϕ^2 related to ϕ (other than squaring ϕ)? **[1]**

_____

11. Use a calculator to evaluate $\dfrac{1}{\phi}$ and write down its value, correct to 5 decimal places. What do you notice? How is $\dfrac{1}{\phi}$ related to ϕ (other than taking the reciprocal of ϕ)? **[1]**

_____

Section C: Perfect Rectangle and Golden Ratio in Real Life

12. Many buildings and structures are shaped like the **Perfect Rectangle** or linked to the **Golden Ratio**. For example, the diagrams below show photos of the Parthenon at Athens. Measure the length and width of the rectangle in the first diagram (must take into account the height of the original roof) and calculate the ratio of its length to its width. What type of rectangle do you get? **[2]**

_____

13. Another example is the Great Pyramid built by the Egyptians in Giza (see below). Calculate the ratio of the "distance up the middle of one side" to the "distance from the edge to the centre". What do you get? **[2]**

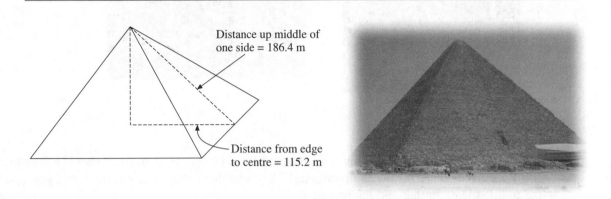

Distance up middle of one side = 186.4 m

Distance from edge to centre = 115.2 m

14. Nature also has some interesting shapes. A nautilus is a creature that lives in the sea and it grows to about 25 cm (see photos below). As its shell develops, it creates one of the most fascinating shapes in mathematics. To see how the shell looks like, an arc of a quadrant is drawn with its centre at the bottom left hand corner of S_8 (see diagram below).

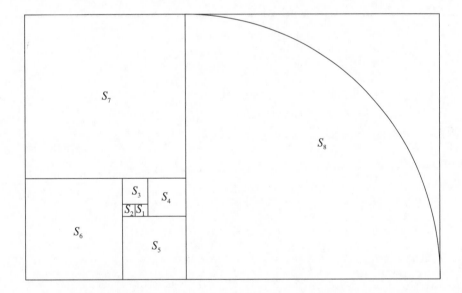

(a) Draw a similar arc for S_7 but with the centre at the ***bottom right hand corner*** of S_7.

(b) Draw a similar arc for S_6 but with the centre at the ***top right hand corner*** of S_6.

(c) Draw a similar arc for S_5 such that the arcs form a curve that spirals inwards.

(d) Continue the process until you reach S_1. **[2]**

Section D: Further Investigation

15. One of the most important questions in any mathematical investigation that you should ask yourself is: ***"What else is there for me to investigate?"*** List one thing related to this topic that you would like to investigate further and investigate it. **[2]**

Question: _____

_____

Answer:

Section E: Conclusion

16. Write down one main lesson that you have learnt from this worksheet. **[1]**

_____

Final Score	16–20	13–15	10–12	7–9	0–6
Grade	A	B	C	D	F

Teacher's Comments (if any):

_____

_____

Non-Routine Problem: Rectangles with Integral Sides

A rectangle with integral sides is a rectangle whose length and breadth are integers. For example, a 3-by-2 rectangle is a rectangle with length 3 units and breadth 2 units. Find all the rectangles with integral sides whose area and perimeter are equal. Show your working clearly.

Scoring Rubric

Competency Level	Heuristics	Mathematical Communication	Answers
4	• Good strategy that lead to correct solutions	• Explanation was clear and complete	
3	• Good strategy with minor errors • Poor strategy but still lead to correct solutions	• Explanation was clear but not complete • Explanation was fairly clear but complete	
2	• Good strategy with major errors • Poor strategy with minor errors	• Explanation was fairly clear but not complete	• Answers were completely correct
1	• Good strategy at the start but unable to proceed any further • Poor strategy with major errors	• Explanation was not clear and not complete	• Answers were partially correct
0	• No evidence of real attempt to solve	• Explanation was irrelevant or no explanation given	• No answers or completely incorrect answers
Score			

Final Score:

☐ / 10

Final Score	8–10	7	5–6	4	0–3
Grade	A	B	C	D	F

Teacher's Comments (if any):

_____

_____

Chapter 9 Volume and Surface Area

Summary

1.　Volume of a right prism = base area × height.

2.　For a cylinder of base radius r and height h, curved surface area = $2\pi rh$, total surface area = $2\pi rh + 2\pi r^2$ or $2\pi r(h + r)$ and volume = $\pi r^2 h$.

Find the volume and total surface area of each of the following solids.

1.　A cube of side 5 cm.

2.　A cube of side 2.4 m.

3.　A rectangular cuboid with length 30 cm, breadth 25 cm and height 12 cm.

4.　A rectangular cuboid with length 1.2 m, breadth 80 cm and height 45 cm.

Find the total surface areas of the following solid cubes given their total volumes.

5.　216 cm^3

6.　0.125 m^3

7.　$42\dfrac{7}{8}$ cm^3

Find the volumes of the following solid cubes given their total surface areas.

8.　1350 m^2

9.　10.14 cm^2

10.　$37\dfrac{1}{2}$ mm^2

Find the number of bricks, each measuring 24 cm by 15 cm by 8 cm that are needed to build straight walls with the following measurements.

11.　12 m long, 30 cm wide and 2.4 m high

12.　33 m long, 48 cm wide and 2.8 m high

13.　20.4 m long, 32 cm wide and 2.25 m high

14.　How much would it cost to build each wall in questions 11 to 13 given that each brick costs 45 cents?

Find the number of 4 cm cubes that can be cut out from the following cuboids whose dimensions are

15.　20 cm by 16 cm by 8 cm,

16.　0.8 m by 0.25 m by 0.35 m,

17.　1.2 m by 85 cm by 0.5 m,

Find the density of each of the following solids given its mass and volume. Give your answers in g/cm^3 correct to 3 significant figures.

18.   mass = 45 g, volume = 8 cm^3

19.   mass = 1.35 kg, volume = 250 cm^3

20.   mass = 0.46 kg, volume = 78 000 mm^3

21.   mass = 0.325 kg, volume = 85 cm^3

Find the volume and total surface area of each of the following solids. All the dimensions given are in centimetres.

22.

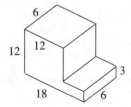

23.

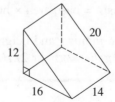

24.

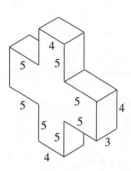

25.

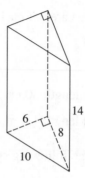

26.

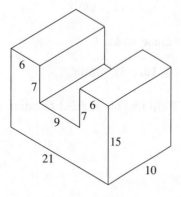

27.

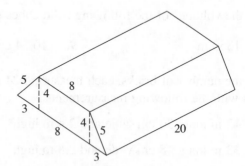

28.   An open rectangular box measuring 28 cm by 20 cm by 12 cm internally is made of wood $\frac{1}{2}$ cm thick. Find
   (a) the capacity of the box in litres,
   (b) the volume of wood used in making the box,
   (c) the mass of the box if the density of the wood used is 1.25 g/cm^3.

29. A closed rectangular box measuring 72 cm by 54 cm by 48 cm externally is made of wood 1.5 cm thick.
Find
(a) the capacity of the box in litres,
(b) the volume of wood used in making the box,
(c) the mass of the box if the density of the wood used is 0.9 g/cm^3.

Find the volume and total surface area of each of the following solid cylinders. (Take $\pi = 3.142$)

30. radius 24 cm, height 21 cm

31. radius 1.45 cm, height 1.4 cm

32. radius 0.28 m, height 45 cm

33. diameter 182 mm, height 7.5 cm

Find the radius of each of the following cylinders. (Take $\pi = 3.142$)

34. volume 2826 cm^3, height 36 cm

35. volume 30.615 cm^3, height 7.8 cm

36. volume 8164 cm^3, height 65 mm

Find the height of each of the following cylinders and give each answer correct to 3 significant figures. (Take $\pi = 3.142$)

37. volume 532 cm^3, radius 5.6 cm

38. volume 20.74 cm^3, radius 2.65 cm

39. volume 0.0054 m^3, radius 15 cm

40. The water in a cylinder, A, of radius 24 cm and height 15 cm is poured into another cylinder, B, of radius 36 cm. Find the height of water in cylinder B.

41. A metal rod of radius 4 cm and length 20 cm weighs 2.3 kg. Find the density of the rod in g/cm^3 and give your answer correct to 3 significant figures. (Take $\pi = 3.142$)

42. The internal and external radii of a hollow metal cylinder are 5 cm and 6 cm respectively. Find the mass of the cylinder if its length is 2.4 m and its density is 7.6 g/cm^3. (Take $\pi = 3.142$)

43. A rectangular trough 8 m long and 3 m wide holds 57.6 m^3 of water. Find the depth of the water in the trough.

44. 2 litres of petrol are poured into a rectangular container 25 cm long, 8 cm wide and 25 cm deep. Find the depth of the petrol in the container.

45. How many 4-centimetres cubes can be cut out of a 12-centimetre cube if there is no wastage in cutting?

46. Each student in a dormitory 12 m long, 7 m wide and 3 m high must have 14 m^3 of air. How many students are allowed to stay in the dormitory?

47. Find the internal height of a cylindrical tank which has an internal cross-sectional area of 400 square centimetres and a capacity of 20 litres.

48. A metal disc, 16 cm in diameter and 3 cm thick, is melted and cast into a cylindrical bar of diameter 4 cm. Find the length of the bar.

49. A piece of butter in the shape of a solid cylinder has a diameter of 6 cm and a length of 10 cm. The butter is remoulded into several circular discs, each 0.8 cm thick and 3 cm in diameter. How many discs can be formed?

50. A cylindrical glass jug, 10 cm in diameter and 27 cm deep, is filled to the brim with water. The water is poured into cylindrical glasses 6 cm in diameter, filling all of them to a depth of 5 cm. How many glasses can be filled?

51. The internal and external diameters of a metal pipe are 6 cm and 7 cm respectively. If the mass of the pipe is 1.3 kg, find the length of the pipe given that the density of the metal is 2.8 g/cm^3. (Take $\pi = 3.142$)

52. The cross-section of a canal is a trapezium which measures 7 m at the top, 5 m at the bottom and has a depth of 2.5 m. Find the volume of water that flows through the canal in 5 seconds if it flows at a speed of 12 km/h.

53. An exhibition hall is rectangular in shape with a hemispherical ceiling. The hall is 80 m long, 30 m wide and 10 m high. Find the volume of air in the hall. (Take $\pi = 3.142$)

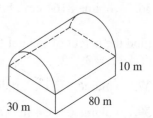

54. Water flows through a pipe of radius 4 cm into a swimming pool 50 m by 25 m. If the pool is flat and the water flows at 18 km/h, how high will the water in the pool be after 100 minutes? Give your answer correct to the nearest mm and take $\pi = 3.142$.

55. A rectangular block of wood is 3.5 m long. Its cross-section is a square of side 35 cm. Find the volume of the biggest possible cylindrical pillar that can be made from it. What volume of the block of wood remains?

56. If 25 mm of rain falls onto a field of area 1.8 ha, what volume of rainwater has fallen onto the field? What is the mass of the water in tonnes if the density of rainwater is 1 g/cm^3?

57. Calculate the capacity in m^3 of a swimming pool 50 m long, 32 m wide, 1.2 m deep for one-fifth of the length and then slopes uniformly downwards to a depth of 3 m.

58. A box 48 cm by 36 cm by 15 cm is packed with solid cubes of side 7 cm and the remaining space is filled with sawdust. Find the volume of sawdust used. If the density of the sawdust is 0.75 g/cm^3, find the mass of sawdust in the box.

59. A rectangular tank measuring 40 cm by 28 cm by 18 cm is empty initially. 12 litres of water are poured into it. Find the height of water in the tank, giving your answer correct to the nearest mm. Find also the total area of the tank that is in contact with the water. Give your answer correct to the nearest cm^2.

60. An open box is 1.4 m long, 0.8 m wide and 55 cm deep internally. It is made of wood 2.5 cm thick. Find the volume of wood used in making the box. If the density of the wood is 950 kg/m^3, find the mass of the empty box. The box is filled to the brim with sand. If the density of the sand is 2.4 g/cm^3, find the total mass of the wood and the sand.

Open-Ended Problem: Cylinder

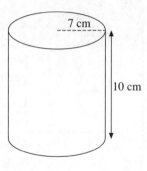

A cylinder is shown on the right. It has a height of 10 cm and a circular cross-section of radius 7 cm. Draw and name as many solids as possible that have some common characteristics with the given cylinder. Write down the characteristics that are common to the given cylinder and the solids you have drawn.

Scoring Rubric

Competency Level	Conceptual Understanding	Creativity	Mathematical Communication
4	• Showed understanding of geometrical properties • Used appropriate mathematical terms	• Included a variety of solids and some original ideas	• Clear and complete names and characteristics given
3	• Showed nearly complete understanding of geometrical properties • Used nearly correct mathematical terms	• Included a variety of solids	• Nearly clear and complete names and characteristics given
2	• Showed understanding of some geometrical properties • Used many wrong mathematical terms	• Included many solids but of limited variety	• Unclear names and characteristics given
1	• Showed very limited understanding of geometrical properties • Misuse of or failure to use mathematical terms	• Included many irrelevant solids	• Gave irrelevant names and characteristics
0	• Showed no understanding of geometrical properties • Failure to use mathematical terms	• Included totally irrelevant solids	• No names and characteristics given
Score			

Final Score:

[ ] / 12

Final Score	10–12	8–9	6–7	4–5	0–3
Grade	A	B	C	D	F

Teacher's Comments (if any):

_____

_____

Term II Revision Test   Time: $1\frac{1}{2}$ h

1. Study the following pattern:

$$1 \times 69 = 69$$
$$2 \times 69 = 138$$
$$4 \times 69 = 276$$
$$8 \times 69 = 552$$
$$16 \times 69 = 1104$$
$$\vdots$$

(a) Write down the next two terms of the sequence
   (i) 1, 2, 4, 8, 16, ...
   (ii) 69, 138, 276, 552, 1104, ...
   Hence write down the next two lines in the pattern shown above.   [4]
(b) The above pattern can be used to find the product of numbers such as 7×69 and 11×69 as shown below:

$$7 = 1 + 2 + 4$$
$$\therefore \quad 7 \times 69 = 69 + 138 + 276 = 483$$
$$11 = 1 + 2 + 8$$
$$\therefore \quad 11 \times 69 = 69 + 138 + 552 = 759$$

In the similar manner, find the product of
   (i) 13×69,
   (ii) 29×69,
   (iii) 76×69.   [6]

2. Solve the equations.
   (a) $19 - 6x = 21 - 9x$
   (b) $2\frac{1}{3}x = 14$
   (c) $13 - 3x - 10 = 3x + 8 - 8x$ [5]

3. (a) When the sum of $2a$ and 15 is divided by 7, the result is 11. Find a.   [3]
   (b) The sum of the ages of Mr Lin and his son is 38 years. In three years' time, Mr Lin will be three times as old as his son. Find their present ages.   [4]

4. (a) A woman buys 60 eggs for $7. Some of the eggs cost 11 cents each and the rest cost 13 cents each. How many of each kind of eggs has she bought?   [3]

(b) A rectangular field 35 metres wide has a fence erected around it. If 160 metres of fencing is used, find the length of the field.   [3]

5. Given that ax $15 - 3x$,
   (a) find the value of x when $a = 4$,
   (b) find the value of a when $x = 4$.   [4]

6. If $8p - 9q = 7q + 3p$, calculate the numerical value of $\frac{2p}{5q}$.   [3]

7. A cylindrical tank of diameter 3.5 m and height 2.6 m is being filled with water from a pipe. If the water flows at a rate of 25 litres per second, how long will it take to fill the tank?   [3]

8. The length of a square is $(2x + 5)$ cm and its perimeter is 52 cm, find its area.   [3]

9. Find the volume of water in a cylindrical tank of diameter 1.4 m and height 60 cm. This water is poured into a rectangular trough of length 1.2 m and width 80 cm. Find the height of water in the trough.
   $\left(\text{Take } \pi = \frac{22}{7}\right)$ [4]

10. In the diagram, AB is the diameter of the large semicircle and OB is the diameter of the small semicircle. Given that $AB = 28$ cm and $OB = 11.2$ cm, calculate the area of the shaded region.
   $\left(\text{Take } \pi = \frac{22}{7}\right)$ [4]

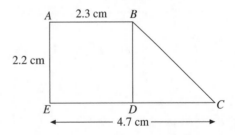

11. Find the area of the trapezium $ABCE$.   [3]

12. Solve the following inequalities.

   (a) $3x < 15 + 5$

   (b) $2x - 4 - (x - 7) > 12$ **[3]**

13. The figure shows a solid block. Find its total surface area and its volume.
(All dimensions are in centimetres.)   **[5]**

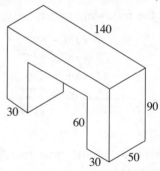

Mid-Year Specimen Paper

*Answer **all** the questions.*　　　　**Time: $2\frac{1}{2}$ h**

1. Evaluate each of the following
    (a) $2\frac{2}{9} - \frac{7}{15} \div 4\frac{1}{5} + \frac{1}{3}$,
    (b) $4\frac{1}{2} + 4\frac{1}{2} \times \frac{2}{3} - \frac{5}{9}$. 　　**[2]**

2. Simplify $3(x - 2y) - 7[x - 3(2y - 7x)]$. 　**[2]**

3. Copy and complete the following number patterns:

    (a) 54, 50, 47, 45, 44, 44, 45, ___, ___ 　**[2]**
    (b) 5, 6, 10, 19, 35, 60, ___, ___ 　**[2]**

4. Given that $a = 2$, $b = 0$, $c = 1$ and $d = -3$, evaluate

    (a) $\dfrac{abc - bcd}{acd + abd}$,

    (b) $\dfrac{ab}{c} - \dfrac{bc}{d} + \dfrac{ad}{2c}$. 　**[4]**

5. Solve the equation $\frac{3}{4}(2x - 1) = \frac{1}{2} + \frac{7x}{8}$.
    　　[3]

6. (a) Write down the value of 27.049 correct to
        (i) two significant figures,
        (ii) one decimal place. 　**[2]**

    (b) Estimate $39.87 \times \sqrt{25.3}$, giving your answer correct to one significant figure.
        　[1]

    (c) Convert $\dfrac{10}{13}$ into a decimal, giving your answer correct to 3 decimal places. 　**[1]**

7. Consider the sequence 5, 9, 13, 17, 21, ...
    (a) Find the 10th term of the sequence.
    (b) Find the nth term of the sequence in terms of n.
    (c) What is the smallest term of the sequence that is greater than 100? 　**[5]**

8. Draw and use the number line to show the following set of numbers: 0, 3, −4, −1.5, 4.6.
    　[2]

9. (a) Arrange the following fractions in ascending order: $\dfrac{5}{6}$, $\dfrac{8}{9}$, $\dfrac{11}{13}$. 　**[2]**

    (b) One number is more than another by 8 and their sum is 230. Find the numbers. 　**[2]**

10. (a) Find the L.C.M. of 12, 28 and 112.
    (b) Find the H.C.F. of 24, 36 and 54. 　**[4]**

11. Bernard is one and a half times as old as Henry. Six years ago, he was twice as old as Henry. How old are the boys now? 　**[4]**

12. A man saves $\dfrac{1}{6}$ of his salary, spends $\dfrac{1}{4}$ of the remainder on rent and the rest on food and other things. What fraction of his salary is spent on food and other things? 　**[3]**

13. Factorise each of the following
    (a) $3x + 18y + 27z$ 　**[1]**
    (b) $2ax - ay + 6bx - 3by$ 　**[2]**

14. Simplify $\frac{2}{3}(x - 4) - \frac{2}{5}(x + 3)$. 　**[2]**

15. A man bought a desktop computer and a printer at a total cost of $2210. If the desktop computer costs $5\frac{1}{2}$ times as much as the printer, find the price of each item. 　**[3]**

16. A metal cylindrical disc of diameter 20 cm and height 4 cm is melted and recast into a thin wire of radius 4 mm. Find the length of the wire. (Take $\pi = 3.142$) 　**[4]**

17. The figure below shows a square of length 14 cm. Calculate the area of the shaded region.

    $\left(\text{Take } \pi = 3\frac{1}{7}\right)$ 　**[4]**

18. Evaluate the following:

(a) $\{[(-4) - (-2) \times 7] + 9 \times 5\} \div 11$ **[2]**

(b) $\dfrac{\left(3\dfrac{1}{2} - 2\dfrac{1}{3}\right)^2}{3\dfrac{1}{2} + 2\dfrac{1}{3}}$ **[2]**

19. State whether each of the following is true or false:

(a) $\dfrac{7}{6}$ is a rational number.

(b) 2.3 is a positive integer.

(c) 189 is a prime number.

(d) π is an irrational number.

(e) There is always a rational number between two irrational numbers.   **[5]**

20. (a) Evaluate each of the following, giving your answer correct to 3 significant figures:

   (i) $\sqrt{12.57} + 3.89^3$

   (ii) $15.76^2 - \dfrac{1}{0.026} \times 76.8$ **[2]**

(b) Simplify
$9a - \{3a - 2[3a(2a + 1) - 2a(3a - 1)]\}$.
   [3]

21. (a) Arrange the following numbers in ascending order.

$\dfrac{3}{7}$, 0.42, 0.4$\dot{2}$8, 0.4$\dot{2}$, 0.$\dot{4}$2$\dot{8}$ **[2]**

(b) A class of 44 pupils sat for a test in science. If the number of pupils who passed the test is three times the number of pupils who failed, find the number of pupils who passed the test.   **[4]**

22. (a) Susan is 10 years older than her brother. In three years' time, she will be twice as old as her brother. What are their present ages?   **[4]**

(b) A man buys s T-shirts at $\$p$ each and sells them at $\$q$ each. What is his profit?   **[3]**

23. (a) Two consecutive numbers are such that the greater number added to twice the smaller number makes a total of 70. Find the numbers.   **[3]**

(b) The difference between two numbers is 9 and their sum is 63. What are the numbers?   **[4]**

24. Complete the next two terms of each of the following sequences.

(a) 2, 6, 11, 17, 24, ____, ____

(b) 1, −4, 9, −16, ____, ____

(c) $\dfrac{5}{7}, \dfrac{3}{4}, \dfrac{7}{9}, \dfrac{4}{5}$, ____, ____

(d) 7, 8, 9, 11, 14, 19, ____   **[4]**

25. Solve the following inequalities.

(a) $3x - (2x - 4) \geq 15$

(b) $\dfrac{1}{4}(3x - 5) \leq x + 2$ **[3]**

Chapter **10** # Ratio, Rate and Speed

---

1. A **ratio** expresses a relationship between two quantities of the same kind. It is usually expressed as a fraction of the first quantity over the second. To find the ratio of two quantities, we must first express them in the same units. A ratio has no unit.

2. A **rate** expresses a relationship between two quantities of different kinds.

3. Average speed of a moving object is given by the formula:

$$\text{Average speed} = \frac{\text{Total distance travelled}}{\text{Total time taken}}$$

4. Conversion of Units:

$$x \text{ km/h} = \frac{(x \times 1000) \text{ m}}{60 \text{ min}} = \frac{1000\,x}{60} \text{ m/min.}$$

$$y \text{ km/h} = \frac{(y \times 1000) \text{ m}}{60 \times 60 \text{ s}} = \frac{1000\,y}{3600} \text{ m/s.}$$

Do not use calculators unless stated otherwise.

Express each of the following ratios in its simplest form.

1.	14 : 35	**2.**	24 : 42	**3.**	144 : 128	**4.**	36 : 132
5.	135 : 240	**6.**	418 : 242	**7.**	192 : 75	**8.**	162 : 384

Express each of the following ratios in its simplest form.

9.	0.25 : 1.5	**10.**	0.09 : 0.21	**11.**	0.84 : 1.12	**12.**	1.44 : 0.48
13.	0.192 : 0.064	**14.**	1.8 : 0.4	**15.**	0.63 : 9.45	**16.**	1.26 : 0.315

Express each of the following ratios in its simplest form.

17. $\dfrac{9}{20} : \dfrac{3}{5}$ **18.** $\dfrac{7}{15} : \dfrac{14}{9}$ **19.** $\dfrac{15}{28} : \dfrac{18}{7}$ **20.** $\dfrac{25}{44} : \dfrac{50}{33}$

21. $1\dfrac{25}{56} : \dfrac{18}{21}$ **22.** $8\dfrac{3}{4} : 3\dfrac{1}{8}$ **23.** $4\dfrac{1}{3} : 65$ **24.** $2.4 : 1\dfrac{1}{5}$

Express the following ratios in their simplest forms.

25. 108 : 36 : 60   **26.** 57 : 19 : 133   **27.** 64 : 96 : 224

28. 1015 : 350 : 455   **29.** 644 : 476 : 140   **30.** 665 : 1995 : 1330

Express the first quantity to the second quantity as a ratio in its lowest terms.

31. 45 cents, $1   **32.** 25 cm, 1.25 m   **33.** 0.25 km, 75 m

34. 0.2 kg, 40 g   **35.** 35 min, 1 h   **36.** 15 min, 2 cm

37. 3.2 h, 72 min   **38.** $0.035 \; \ell$, $105 \; \text{cm}^3$

Divide $336 in the following ratios.

39. 1 : 5   **40.** 5 : 3   **41.** 5 : 7   **42.** 3 : 11

43. 5 : 9   **44.** 3 : 13   **45.** 8 : 13   **46.** 10 : 11

47. 11 : 13   **48.** 7 : 17

49. $180 is shared among three people in the ratio $x : y \; z$. Calculate **(a)** the smallest share, **(b)** the largest share, given that
     (a) $x = 1, y = 2, z = 6$ **(b)** $x = 2, y = 3, z = 5$ **(c)** $x = 1, y = 4, z = 7$
     (d) $x = 3, y = 1, z = 11$ **(e)** $x = 4, y = 11, z = 3$ **(f)** $x = 2, y = 13, z = 5$

50. The ratio of the number of motor cars to that of motor cycles is 9 : 4. Calculate the number of motor cars in the car-park given that the number of motor cycles in the car-park is
     (a) 16,   **(b)** 32,   **(c)** 40,   **(d)** 28.

51. A sum of money is divided in the ratio 3 : 5 : 9. Calculate the smallest share given that the largest share is
     (a) $54,   **(b)** $108,   **(c)** $369,   **(d)** $558.

52. In a quadrilateral, $ABCD$, the angles A, B and C are in the ratio 1 : 3 : 7. Find **(a)** $\hat{D}$, **(b)** $\hat{C}$, given that the sum of $\hat{A}$, $\hat{B}$ and $\hat{C}$ is
     (a) 187°,   **(b)** 242°,   **(c)** 275°.

53. A sum of money is divided among three people in the ratio 15 : 18 : 7. Find **(a)** the total sum of money, **(b)** the largest share, given that the smallest share is
     (a) $84,   **(b)** $133,   **(c)** $301,   **(d)** $3990.

54. Find the difference between the largest share and the smallest share when $160 is shared among three people in the following ratios.
   (a) $1 : 6 : 9$ **(b)** $2 : 5 : 13$ **(c)** $22 : 5 : 13$ **(d)** $32 : 11 : 37$

55. A sum of money is divided among Peter, Paul and Jane in the ratio $13 : 12 : 7$. Calculate how much Paul gets if the amount Peter gets more than Jane is
   (a) $78,   **(b)** $126,   **(c)** $360,   **(d)** $540.

56. An alloy consists of three metals, X, Y and Z. Calculate the ratio $X : Z$ given that
   (a) $X : Y = 2 : 3$ and $Y : Z = 5 : 4$,   **(b)** $X : Y = 5 : 7$ and $Y : Z = 13 : 10$,
   (c) $X : Y = 7 : 3$ and $Y : Z = 11 : 21$,   **(d)** $X : Y = 8 : 15$ and $Y : Z = 21 : 32$,

57. 60 kg of inferior vegetable oil is mixed with 135 kg of superior vegetable oil. Find the ratio in which the superior vegetable oil is mixed with the inferior vegetable oil, leaving your answer in its simplest form.

58. John is 1.68 m tall whereas his younger brother is 105 cm tall. Express the ratio of John's height to his brother's height in its simplest form.

59. 126 parts of pure gold are mixed with 42 parts of an alloy. Find the ratio of the total number of parts to the number of parts of
   (a) pure gold,   **(b)** alloy.
   Hence, write down the ratio in which the alloy is mixed with pure gold.

60. The length and breadth of a hall are 28 m and 21 m respectively. If the ratio of its length to its height is $7 : 6$, find the height and the ratio of its breadth to its height.

61. The salaries of A and B are in the ratio $8 : 3$. The salaries of B and C are in the ratio $5 : 12$. Express the salaries of A, B and C in the form of a ratio.

62. Two types of rice are sold in the market. One of them is sold at 10 kg for $9.20 whereas the other type is sold at 5 kg for $6.90. Find the ratio of their prices.

63. A rectangle measures 32 cm by 24 cm. Given that its measurements are increased in the ratio $5 : 4$ to obtain a second rectangle, find the ratio of their
   (a) perimeters,   **(b)** areas.

64. Express 40 minutes after 5.55 p.m. using the 24-hour clock notation.

65. A train leaves Town A at 22 17 and arrives in Town B at 07 17 the next day. How long does the whole journey take?

66. A bus leaves Town X at 21 30 and arrives in Town Y at 08 00 the next day. Calculate
   (a) the time taken for the journey,
   (b) the average speed of the bus, given that the distance from Town X to Town Y is 651 km.

67. Peter was supposed to meet Paul one evening at 19 50. Paul arrived at the exact time but Peter arrived at a quarter to ten. Who arrived first? For how long did one wait for the other?

68. A car is parked in a car-park from 07 45 to 16 30 on the same day. Find
    (a) the total time for which the car is parked,
    (b) the parking fee if the rate of charges is $2.50 for the first hour and 80 cents for each half hour or part of a half hour thereof.

69. It takes a cyclist 44 minutes to cycle a distance of 11 km.
    (a) How long will it take him to cycle a distance of
        (i) 45 km,   **(ii)** 36 km,   **(iii)** 20 km?
    (b) What is the speed of the cyclist in km/h?

70. Mr Chai leaves his house at 08 37 and travels by motor cycle to the railway station which 27 km away. If he arrives at the station 36 minutes later, find the average speed at which he travels in km/h. How long will he have to wait if the train, due at 09 42, is 11 minutes late?

71. A family travelled from Singapore to Penang. Shown below is a copy of their timetable.

From	To	Time Required
Singapore	Johor Baru	40 min
		30 min (breakfast)
Johor Baru	Kuala Lumpur	5 h 35 min
		55 min (lunch)
Kuala Lumpur	Ipoh	3 h 12 min
Ipoh	Penang	1 h 58 min

    Given that they left Singapore at 05 30, when did they arrive in Penang?

Find the value of x in each of the following cases.

72. $3 : 9 = 4 : x$ **73.** $4 : 3 = x : 6$ **74.** $5 : 11 = 10 : x$

75. $x : 5.7 = 8 : 12$ **76.** $14 : 9 = 7 : x$ **77.** $12 : 25 = x : 5$

78. If 20 m^2 of flooring cost $36,
    (a) find the cost of
        (i) 25 m^2,   **(ii)** 55 m^2, of flooring.
    (b) what area of the same flooring can be bought for
        (i) $63,   **(ii)** $75.60?

79. 12 ceramic tiles cost $32.40.
    (a) Find the cost of
        (i) 15 tiles,   **(ii)** 80 tiles.
    (b) How many tiles can be bought for
        (i) $86.40,   **(ii)** $48.60,   **(iii)** $162,   **(iv)** $118.80?

80. A bus company charges $1.35 a kilometre to charter a bus which carries 54 children. How much should each child be charged if the distance to be covered is 50 km?

81. My car travels 128 km on 12 litres of petrol. How far do I expect it to travel on a full tank of 30 litres?

82. A motorist plans to travel 1273 km. If petrol costs $1.18 per litre and his car travels 19 km on 1 litre of petrol, how much will he need to spend on petrol for the trip?

83. A telephone bill consists of a monthly rental fee of $12.50 and charges resulting from the number of calls made at 2 cents per call. In a particular month, Miss Chen made 493 calls. How much was her bill? In another particular month, Mr Li paid a bill of $20.06. How many calls did he make in that month?

84. It costs 9 tourists $1620 to stay at a hotel for 4 days. Find
    (a) the cost of staying at the same hotel for 6 days for 15 tourists,
    (b) the number of days 10 tourists can stay at the hotel for $2250.

85. A train left Town *A* at 08 45 and arrived at Town *B* at 15 10.
    (a) How long did the journey take?
    (b) Find the distance between Town *A* and Town *B* given that the speed of the train was 108 km/h.

86. A motorist starts travelling at 23 17 on a 172-km journey. At what time will he arrive at his destination given that he travels at an average speed of 48 km/h?

87. If light can travel 31 times around the world in 4 seconds, how many times can it circle the world in 10 seconds?

88. A man eats 200 g of rice a day and he has enough rice to last him 35 days. How long would the stock of rice last him if he were to eat 250 g of rice a day.

89. A motorist starts to travel on a 272-km journey at 11 13. At what time will he reach his destination given that he travels at an average speed of 64 km/h. He leaves at 17 55 for the return journey and arrives at the starting point at 23 35. Calculate the time taken and the average speed for the return journey.

90. A rectangular brass sheet of length 1.5 m and breadth 75 cm weights 7.2 kg. Find the area, in m², of another similar sheet of brass weighing 12.8 kg.

91. A man travelling by car at an average speed of 70 km/h completes a journey in 54 minutes. On his return journey, he travels at an average speed of 45 km/h.
    (a) How long does the return journey take?
    (b) If he begins his outwards journey at 09 55 and rests for 40 minutes before making his return journey, at what time does he arrive at the initial starting point?

92. 45 men working 8 hours a day can finish a project within a given time. Five men unable to report for work. How long should the rest work a day to finish the project on time?

93. Given that 224 hours of work need to be done to complete a project.
    (a) How long will it take 4 men, each working an 8-hour day to complete the project?
    (b) If each of them is paid $7.50 per hour, how much will it cost to employ them altogether?
    (c) How many hours of overtime must they put in per day if the project to be completed in 4 days?
    (d) Given that the overtime rate of payment is $1\frac{1}{2}$ times as much as the regular hourly rate, find the cost of the project now.

94. 10 cooks working for 8 hours each can prepare a meal for 536 people. How many cooks will be needed to prepare a meal for 737 people if they are required to prepare the meal in 5 hours?

95. A contractor agrees to lay a road 3000 m long in 30 days. He employs 50 men who work for 8 hours a day. After 20 working days, he finds that only 1200 m of the road is completed. How many more men are to be employed to finish the work on time if each man now works 10 hours a day?

Non-Routine Problem: The Amazing Race

In a 100-metre race, Edwin beats Beng Seng by 10 metres. The two boys plan to have another race. Edwin will start 10 metres behind the start line this time.

(a) If both boys run at the same rate as before, who will win the race? Or is it a draw?
(b) If someone wins the second race, then he wins by how many metres?

Show your working clearly.

Hint: There is a method that does **not** involve algebra.

Scoring Rubric

Competency Level	Heuristics	Mathematical Communication	Answers
4	• Good strategy that lead to correct solutions	• Explanation was clear and complete	
3	• Good strategy with minor errors • Poor strategy but still lead to correct solutions	• Explanation was clear but not complete • Explanation was fairly clear but complete	
2	• Good strategy with major errors • Poor strategy with minor errors	• Explanation was fairly clear but not complete	• Both answers were correct
1	• Good strategy at the start but unable to proceed any further • Poor strategy with major errors	• Explanation was not clear and not complete	• First answer correct but second answer wrong • Second answer correct but first answer wrong due to careless mistake
0	• No evidence of real attempt to solve	• Explanation was irrelevant or no explanation given	• No answers or completely incorrect answers
Score			

Final Score:

 / 10

Final Score	8–10	7	5–6	4	0–3
Grade	A	B	C	D	F

Teacher's Comments (if any):

_____

_____

1. A percentage is a fraction whose denominator is 100 and we use % to represent percent. A percentage can be converted to a fraction by dividing its value by 100.

2. Discount = Original Selling price – Sale price

Write each percentage as a fraction in its simplest form.

1. 210%   **2.** 4.8%   **3.** 18%   **4.** 0.25%   **5.** $1\frac{1}{3}\%$

Express the following as decimals.

6. 99%   **7.** 300%   **8.** $2\frac{4}{5}\%$ **9.** 0.68%   **10.** 1.002%

Convert the following into percentages.

11. $\frac{3}{4}$ **12.** $\frac{2}{5}$ **13.** $\frac{6}{25}$ **14.** $\frac{19}{20}$ **15.** $\frac{12}{15}$

Convert the following into percentages.

16. 0.07   **17.** 0.058   **18.** 0.14

19. 0.027   **20.** 0.5218   **21.** 2.43

Express the first quantity as a percentage of the second.

22. $14, $42   **23.** 33 cm, 3.96 m   **24.** $4.40, 99 cents

25. 45 kg, 36 kg   **26.** 6 h, 1 day   **27.** 20 min, 1 h

28. 175 mℓ, 1 ℓ   **29.** 48 cents, $1.44   **30.** 2 yr, 18 mth

Find the value of the following.

31. $66\frac{2}{3}\%$ of 72 litres   **32.** 45% of 4 kg   **33.** 7.5% of $2500

34. $37\frac{1}{2}\%$ of 56 cm   **35.** $33\frac{1}{3}$ of 48 m   **36.** 20.6% of 5000 people

Increase

37. $60 by 10%,

38. 32 g by $12\frac{1}{2}$ %,

39. 18 m² by 5%,

40. 50 m by 125%,

Decrease

41. $88 by 5%,

42. 64 g by $12\frac{1}{2}$ %

43. 124 litres by 25%,

44. 225 m by 16%,

Find the value of x in each of the following.

45. 12% of x is 48

46. $29\frac{1}{2}$ % of x is 295

47. $66\frac{2}{3}$ of x is 432

48. 77.5% of x is 217

49. 43.75% of x is 49

50. 124% of x is 155

51. In a box of 180 oranges, 15% were spoilt. How many oranges were in good condition?

52. A school has 1500 pupils. On a particular day, 3% of them were late for school. Find the number of pupils who were late for school.

53. The price of a notebook increases from 60 cents to 75 cents. Find the percentage increase in price.

54. In a constituency, there are 12 000 eligible voters. In a particular election, the following results were obtained.

Candidate	Percentage of votes
A	7%
B	39%
C	42%

Find the actual number of voters for each candidate given that 12% of them did not vote.

55. A factory has 1600 workers and the percentages of workers absent from work from Monday to Friday in a certain week are given below.

Day	Percentage of absentees
Monday	15%
Tuesday	1.5%
Wednesday	10%
Thursday	5%
Friday	7%

Find the number of workers who turn up for work on each day.

56. A container contains 30 ℓ of a mixture of which 9 ℓ is water, the rest being milk. Find the percentage of water and of milk in the container.

57. A 60-kg ingot of brass, consisting of zinc and copper, contains 15% zinc. How many kilograms of copper does the 60-kg ingot of brass contain?

58. A fruit dealer bought a carload of apples weighing 1245 kg. After sorting, he discovered that 83 kg of them were spoiled. Find the percentage of unspoiled apples.

59. The Chen family's expenses for a particular month is given as follows:

Item	Expenditure
rent	$169
food	$273
clothing	$52
transportation	$65
miscellaneous	$91

Calculate each expenditure as a percentage of the total expenditure.

60. A television set is sold for $1998 and a 11% profit is made. Find the original cost of the television set.

61. A dealer sells a camera to a man and makes a 15% profit. The man sells the camera to another man for $414 at a loss of 10%. Find the original price of the camera.

62. At what price must an article which costs $450 be sold in order to make a profit of $16\frac{1}{2}$ %?

63. A cash discount of 8% is allowed on an item which costs $45. How much money is saved if a customer decides to pay in cash? How much more can he save if the discount is 9%?

64. Mr Liu intends to make a new fence for his garden. He buys 5 wooden panels at $25 each, 6 wooden posts at $12 each, 1 drill bit at $10, 12 bolts at $15 for six and 300 g of nails at $10 per kg. Find the total amount he has to pay given that he is allowed a discount of 10% before adding a 15% value-added tax on the amount after the discount.

65. A door-to-door salesman is paid a basic salary of $520 per month plus a commission of 25% of total sales made during the month. If he sells $5264 worth of goods in a particular month, find his total income for that month.

66. The cash price for a personal computer is $3600. Mr Li buys such a computer on monthly terms by paying a deposit of 30% of the cash price followed by 24 monthly instalments of $125 each.
    (a) How much deposit does Mr Li pay?
    (b) Find the total amount of the 24 monthly instalments.
    (c) How much more does Mr Li have to pay? Express this amount as a percentage of the cash price.

67. A Nicam stereo colour television set is priced at $1800. It can be bought on the following hire purchase terms: 25% deposit, interest rate of 18% per annum, repayment period of 2 years in equal monthly instalmments.
    (a) Find the amount of each monthly instalment. (b) What is the total hire purchase price?

68. James earned $36 000 in the year 1990. If he pays a 15% federal tax, an 8% state tax and a 3% city tax, how much money is left for James after the deductions are made?

69. In a certain town, the property tax is 3% of the assessed valuation of the property. What is the assessed value of a piece of property which pays $7200 in taxes a year?

70. A telephone bill reads as follows:

Cost of calls plus rental..	$30
Service charge...	10%
Government tax (on calls plus rental, service charge)....	15%

    Calculate the total bill.

71. In a school, there are 3 classes of students who do Additional Mathematics. There are 42 students in class A and 40 students in class B. Given that the students in class A constitutes 35% of the total number of students taking Additional Mathematics, find the number of students in class C.

72. Of the candidates from a certain school who sat for the Mathematics examination at 'A' level, 18% obtained grade A, 38% obtained grade B and the rest obtained grade C. Find the total number of candidates given that 77 candidates obtained grade C.

73. The ABC Dress Company determines the selling price of its dresses by adding 32% to the cost. Calculate the selling price of a garment that costs $25.

74. A trader mixes 2 kg of butter which costs $8 per kg with 3kg of butter which costs $6 per kg. He sells the mixture at $2.55 per 250 g. Find his percentage gain.

75. Two types of coffee, one costing $9 per kg and the other costing $13 per kg, are mixed in the ratio 3 : 1. The mixture is sold at $1.25 pr 100 g. Find the percentage gain.

76. A dealer gains $18\frac{3}{4}$ % by selling a microwave oven for $950. Find the cost price of the oven. What percentage profit would he get if he were to sell it for $1050?

77. A man bought a flat for $76 000 and a second-hand car for $27 500. He sold the flat at a gain of 15% and the car at a loss of 12%. Find the total amount gained or lost from the two transactions.

78. By selling a particular sets of books for $408, a bookseller suffers a loss of 4%. Find the cost price of the books. What is the percentage gain or loss if the books are sold for $510?

79. The cost of manufacturing an article is $160. The manufacturer sells it to a dealer at a gain of 45% and the dealer sells it to a purchaser for $266.80. Find the dealer's percentage gain.

80. To pay for his petrol on a car trip in France, a Singapore student studying in England changes £80 into francs at the rate of 9.90 francs to the £. How many francs will he receive?

Real-life Performance Task: Are You Making a Sound Investment?

The table below lists prices, in dollars, for one share of stock in several companies. An entry like 29.15 means $29.15 per share.

1. Complete the *Difference* and *Percentage Change* columns of the table. **[4]**

Stock	Close One Year Ago	Close Today	Difference	Percentage Change (to 4 s.f.)
AdCo	29.15	32.75	3.6	12.35%
BenPower	25.25	28	2.75	10.89%
Creativity	43	35.88	−7.12	−16.56%
Danny	19.25	18.5	−0.75	−3.896%
EngCo	38.75	48.13		
FrenChic	13.5	11		
GinMotor	44.75	43.25		
HiMart	18	22.75		
iTEL	30.88	29.13		
JogEquip	42.63	45		
KitMart	15.63	16.25		
LanNet	28.75	37		

2. Suppose you had $2000 to invest in shares one year ago and you bought the biggest number of *Creativity* shares that you could buy with the $2000. How many *Creativity* shares did you own?
   Note: You cannot buy a fraction of a share **[1]**

3. Did you earn or lose as of today? And by how much? Show 2 methods of calculation: one using the *Difference* column and the other using the *Percentage Change* column of the table above.

    [3]

    _____

    _____

4. (a) Which share gains the most in terms of money value?   **[1]**

    _____

    (b) Which share gains the most in terms of percentage change?   **[1]**

    _____

    (c) Is your answer in (a) and (b) the same? Why or why not?   **[2]**

    _____

    _____

5. If you have foresight one year ago, how would you invest your $2000? Which share should you have bought? Should you choose the share with the biggest gain in terms of money value or in terms of percentage change? Why? How much would you have earned?   **[4]**

    _____

    _____

    _____

6. If you had $2000 to invest today, which share(s) do you think you would buy? Explain your decision.   **[2]**

    _____

    _____

Final Score:

Final Score	15–18	12–14	9–11	6–8	0–5
Grade	A	B	C	D	F

☐ / 18

Teacher's Comments (if any):

_____

_____

New Syllabus Mathematics Workbook 1

Chapter 12 Functions and Graphs

Summary

1. A Cartesian plane consists of two axes, the **x-axis** and the **y-axis**, intersecting at right angles at the **origin** $O(0, 0)$.

2. An ordered pair (a, b) locates a point P in the Cartesian plane, a being the **x-coordinate** and b the **y-coordinate** of P.

3. A function is a relationship that expresses a dependent variable in terms of an independent variable and each value of the independent variable will produce a unique value for the dependent variable.

4. The gradient of a straight line is a measure of the ratio of the vertical change to the horizontal change.

Practice Questions

1. Write down the coordinates of the points in the diagram below.

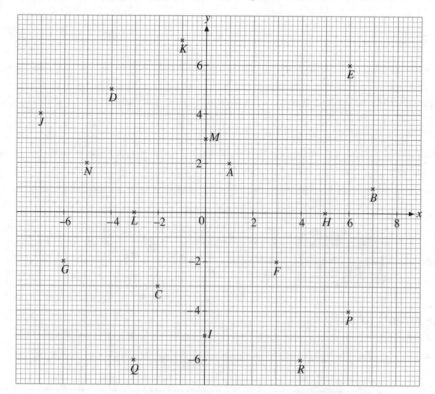

2. Using a scale of 1 cm to represent 1 unit on both the *x*- and *y*-axes, draw the *x*- and *y*-axes for $-8 \le x \le 8$ and $-8 \le y \le 8$. Plot and label the following points.

$A(2, 4)$, $B(3, 8)$, $C(-2, 5)$, $D(-7, -4)$, $E(6, -2)$, $F(-4, 0)$
$G(-3, -5)$, $H(-8, 1)$, $I(-4, 3)$, $J(8, -1)$, $K(1, 1)$, $L(0, 6)$
$M(6, -5)$, $N(0, -7)$, $O(-5, -5)$, $P(7, -4)$, $Q(4, 6)$, $R(-2, -4)$

3. Plot each set of the given points on a graph paper. Join the points in the given sequence straight lines and name the geometrical shapes obtained.
    (a) $A(1, 1)$, $B(7, 1)$, $C(4, 8)$
    (b) $P(1, 3)$, $Q(3, 5)$, $R(7, 1)$
    (c) $D(1, 1)$, $E(7, -1)$, $F(8, 2)$, $G(2, 5)$
    (d) $P(-5, 3)$, $Q(-2, 4)$, $R(0, 3)$, $S(3, -1)$
    (e) $L(-1, -2)$, $M(1, 3)$, $N(-1, 4)$, $K(-3, 3)$
    (f) $W(0, 2)$, $X(3, 0)$, $Y(1, -3)$, $Z(-2, -1)$
    (g) $A(-1, -3)$, $B(3, -4)$, $C(6, 2)$, $D(2, 3)$
    (h) $P(-4, -1)$, $Q(-2, -4)$, $R(-4, -7)$, $S(-6, -4)$

4. Plot the vertices of $\triangle ABC$ on a piece of graph paper where $A(-2, 1)$, $B(6, 5)$, $C(6, 2)$. Calculate the area of $\triangle ABC$.

5. Find the gradients of the lines l_1, l_2 and l_3.

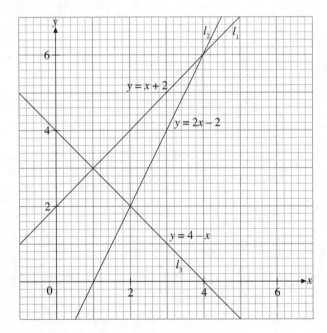

6. Find the gradients of the lines *AB*, *BC* and *AC*.

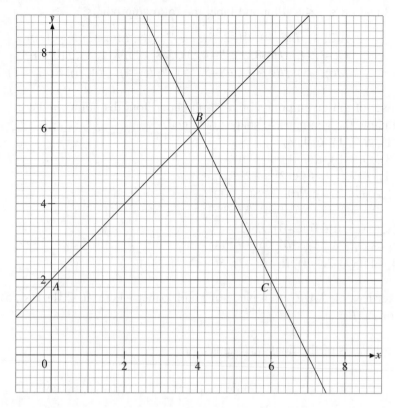

7. Find the gradients of the lines *PQ*, *PR* and *QR*.

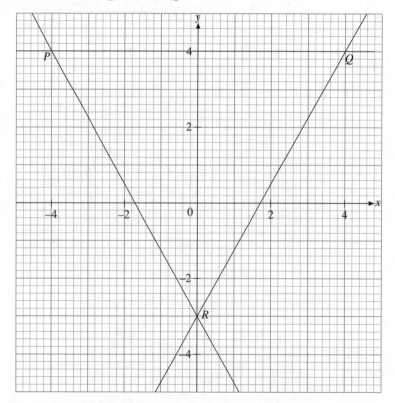

8. The vertices of $\triangle PQR$ are $P(0, -4)$, $Q(4, -2)$ and $R(2, 2)$.
   (a) Plot the point S such that $PQRS$ is a square.
   (b) Find the gradients of PQ and QR and SR.
   (c) What do you notice about the gradients of PQ and SR?

9. Given the function $y = 2 - x$, copy and complete the table below.

x	0	1	2	3
y	2			

   Draw the graph of $y = 2 - x$ for values of x from 0 to 3. What is the gradient of the linear function $y = 2 - x$?

10. Given the linear function $y = \frac{1}{2}x + 1$, copy and complete the table below.

x	-4	0	2	4
y		1		

   (a) Draw the graph of $y = \frac{1}{2}x + 1$ for values of x from -4 to 4.

   (b) Does the points $(3, 2.5)$ and $\left(-1, -\frac{1}{2}\right)$ lie on the line?

   (c) Find the coordinates of the points where the line cuts the x-axis.

   (d) Find the gradient of the line $y = \frac{1}{2}x + 1$.

11. Given the vertices of a quadrilateral $PQRS$ are $P(-4, 3)$, $Q(-2, 6)$, $R(1, 7)$ and $S(4, 1)$.
    (a) Draw the quadrilateral $PQRS$ on a piece of graph paper.
    (b) Find the gradients of the lines PQ, QR, RS and PS.
    (c) Write down the coordinates of the point where PS cuts the y-axis.

12. The equations of the lines l_1 and l_2 are $y = \frac{1}{2}x + 3$ and $y + x = 6$ respectively.
    (a) Draw the graphs of l_1 and l_2 for x from -4 to 6.
    (b) Find the gradients of l_1 and l_2.
    (c) Write down the coordinates of the point when l_1 cuts l_2.

13. The charge $\$y$ of an electrician attending a house call job is given by $y = 35 + 15x$ where x is the number of hours spent on the job. Copy and complete the following table.

x	0	1	2	3	4
y	35				

   (a) Draw the graph of $y = 35 + 15x$ for $x = 0$ to $x = 4$.

(b) Use your graph to find the charge for a job lasting 2.5 hours.

(c) The charge of a job is $90. Find the time taken to complete the job.

(d) Find the gradient of the graph and state the practical meaning of the gradient.

14. A frozen chicken is taken out from the freezer. Its temperature $y°C$ at time x hours after it is taken out from the freezer is given by the function $y = -5 + 6x$ for $0 \leq x \leq 5$.

(a) Copy and complete the table for $y = -5 + 6x$.

x	0	1	2	3	4	5
y	–5	1				

(b) Draw the graph of $y = -5 + 6x$ for $0 \leq x \leq 5$.

(c) Find the temperature of the chicken when $x = 2.5$.

(d) When will the temperature of the chicken be 16°C?

(e) Find the gradient of the line $y = -5 + 6x$ and explain the physical meaning of the gradient?

(f) What is the physical meaning of –5 in the equation $y = -5 + 6x$?

Your friend is absent from school for a few days and he or she is not clear about the meaning of the gradient of a straight line. Explain to your friend, in your own words, what you understand by the phrase 'gradient of a straight line'. You may draw diagrams to illustrate. You need to elaborate what is meant by a bigger or smaller gradient, and what is meant by a positive or negative gradient. You also need to link gradient to *real-life examples* such as the gradient of a road or a hill.

Scoring Rubric

Competency Level	Conceptual Understanding	Mathematical Communication
4	• Showed complete understanding of the mathematical concepts involved • Used appropriate mathematical terms	• Gave clear and complete conclusions
3	• Showed nearly complete understanding of the mathematical concepts involved • Used nearly correct mathematical terms	• Gave fairly complete conclusions
2	• Showed understanding of some of the mathematical concepts involved • Used some wrong mathematical terms	• Gave vague conclusions
1	• Showed limited understanding of the mathematical concepts involved • Misuse of or failure to use mathematical terms	• Gave conclusions which were difficult to understand
0	• Showed no understanding of the mathematical concepts involved • Failure to use mathematical terms	• Gave muddled conclusions
Score		

Final Score:

☐ / 8

Final Score	7–8	6	4–5	3	0–2
Grade	A	B	C	D	F

Teacher's Comments (if any):

_____

_____

Chapter 13 Statistics

Summary

1. (a) Numerical data can be obtained in many ways.
   (b) The data collected can be summarised in a systematic way by tabulation.
   (c) The tabulated data can be presented in a graphical form.
   (d) Some common statistical graphs are **pictograms**, **bar graphs**, **pie charts** and **line graphs**.

2. (a) A set of data, or raw data, can be arranged in an orderly way in the form of a **frequency table**.
   (b) A frequency table can be represented graphically by a **histogram**.
   (c) A **histogram** is a vertical bar graph with **no space** in between the bars.
   (d) The **area** of each bar is proportional to the frequency it represents.

3. Suitable choice of statistical graphs depends on the type of data that is collected. In general,
   (a) a pictogram is most suitable when the data needs to be presented in a lively and interesting manner while the accuracy is not of utmost importance;
   (b) a bar graph and a histogram are useful for comparing the data clearly;
   (c) a pie chart is suitable when we need to compare the proportion of a whole rather than the actual numerical values;
   (d) a line graph is most suitable to show data that changes with time.

Practice Questions

1. The following pictogram illustrates the daily production of cars in a factory for one week:

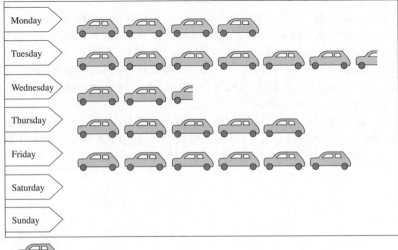

represents 20 cars

New Syllabus Mathematics Workbook 1

(a) How many cars would be represented by drawings of

    (i) 3 cars,   (ii) $4\frac{1}{2}$ cars?

(b) How many cars would be drawn to represent
    (i) 160 cars,   (ii) 110 cars?

(c) How many cars were produced on
    (i) Tuesday,   (ii) Thursday,   (iii) Saturday?

(d) On what day was the production greatest?

(e) Production stopped for half a day due to a fault in the machinery. Which day was that?

(f) How many more cars were produced on Tuesday than on Monday?

(g) Give a reason why there were no cars produced on Saturday and Sunday.

(h) Find the total number of cars produced for the week.

2.

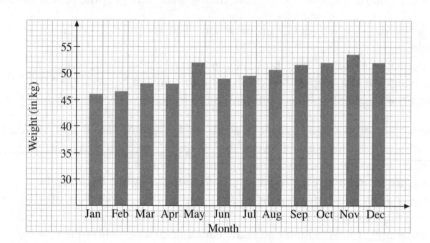

The bar chart above shows the weight of a boy recorded on the first day of each month.

(a) What was his weight on the first day of
    (i) March   (ii) July   (iii) October?

(b) On the first day of which month was his weight
    (i) 46.5 kg   (ii) 49 kg   (iii) 50.5 kg?

(c) When was he heaviest for the year recorded?

(d) At the beginning of which three months were his weights the same?

(e) Find the difference between his *lightest* and his *heaviest* recorded weights.

(f) There were only two occasions when he lost weight.
    (i) If his greater loss in weight was caused by illness, in what month was he ill?
    (ii) He started to go on a diet when he realised that he was putting on weight. In what month did his diet program show?

(g) Only once during the year did his weight exceed 53 kg. What month was that?

(h) Display the boy's weight using a line graph. Which of the two forms of display do you think is more suitable in helping you answer the above questions? Why?

3. The line graph displays the number of pupils attending the Drama Club meeting during a school term.

(a) In which week was the attendance greatest?

(b) Once during the term the attendance was the same in two consecutive weeks. Which weeks were they?

(c) The Club stopped the weekly meeting during the week in which the school examination was held. Which week was it?

(d) Give a possible reason why the attendance in the 8th week was the smallest.

(e) Find the percentage drop in attendance from the 7th week to the 8th week.

(f) Before the school examination, between which weeks was there the greatest increase in attendance? Find this increase.

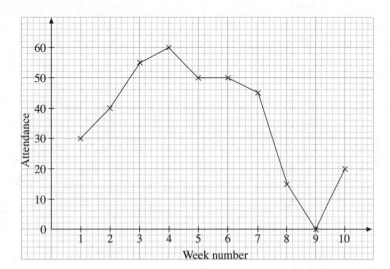

4. The bar chart shows the sales of a company over a number of years.

(a) What was the value of sales in

    (i) 2002

    (ii) 2004

    (iii) 2006?

(b) In what year was the value of sales $1 000 000?

(c) Between which years was there the greatest increase in the value of sales? What was the increase in the value of sales?

(d) In 2005 the sales target was $1 300 000. By how much did the company exceed its target? Express this as a percentage of the sales target.

(e) In 2006 the sales target was $1 650 000. By how much did the company fall short of its target?

Express this as a percentage of the value of sales in 2006.

(f) Find the total value of sales over the 6 years.

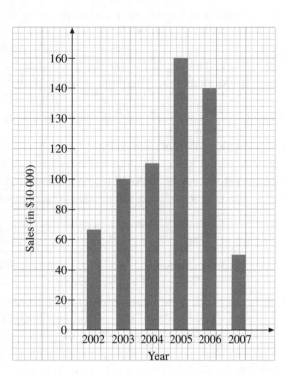

5. The line graph shows the temperature in a classroom recorded each morning for ten consecutive days.
    (a) During the period it rained throughout the day on one occasion. What day was it? What was the temperature of the classroom on that morning?
    (b) On which day was it warmest? What was the temperature on that day?
    (c) On how many days was the temperature below 29°C?
    (d) For what fraction of the days was the temperature above 28°C?

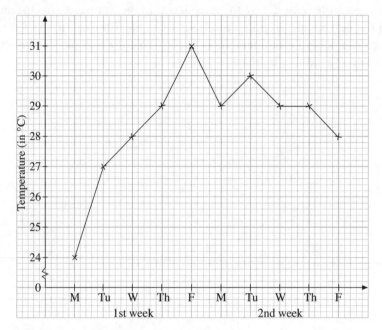

6. Draw a pictogram to illustrate the information below.

Daily takings of ABC Pte Ltd:

Monday	Tuesday	Wednesday	Thursday	Friday	Saturday	Sunday
$4500	$6000	$6500	$7000	$12 000	$8000	Nil

Scale: (\$) represents $1000

7. A study was made on the absenteeism in a school. As part of the findings, the table below shows the number of students present in a class of 42 for a week.

Day	Monday	Tuesday	Wednesday	Thursday	Friday
Number present	42	36	40	36	38

    (a) Draw a bar chart to show the information above.
    (b) On what day were no students absent?
    (c) What fraction of students were absent on Friday?
    (d) Was any student absent for the whole week?

8. Baby Quiqui was weighed at the beginning of each month for ten months.

Month	1	2	3	4	5	6	7	8	9	10
Weight (in kg)	3.7	3.8	4.7	5.4	6.6	8.2	8.3	8.2	8.7	9.4

(a) Draw a line graph to show this information.
(b) Between which months was there the greatest increase in Baby Quiqui's weight?
(c) In which month was there a decrease in Baby Quiqui's weight?
(d) Calculate Baby Quiqui's average weight for the ten months?

9. The table shows the hours of work (in thousands) put in by the workers at Saturn Electronics' factory for the year 1998–2007.

Year	1998	1999	2000	2001	2002	2003	2004	2005	2006	2007
Number of hours (in 1000 hours)	204	172	176	182	184	158	98	128	172	200

Draw a line graph based on the information above.
(a) In which years were there a fall in the number of working hours?
(b) In which year was the fall in working hours the greatest and in which year was the fall the least?
(c) In which years were there an increase in the working hours?
(d) In which year was the increase in working hours the greatest and in which year was the increase the least?
(e) In which years were the number of working hours above 172 000?

10. The following advertisement put up by a gourmet coffee chain claimed that its sales have increased by 300% from 2003 to 2006.

Explain briefly whether the advertisement is misleading.

2003

2006

Calculate the angles on a pie chart corresponding to items *A*, *B*, *C*, *D* and *E* given in the tables below:

11.

Item	A	B	C	D	E
Number	9	6	8	12	5

12.

Item	A	B	C	D	E
Number	102	64	24	10	40

13. The pie chart shows the exports of Guanticca in 2007.
    (a) What was the ratio of manufactured goods to mineral exported by Guanticca in 2007?
    (b) What was the ratio of agricultural produce to manufactured goods exported?
    (c) If the total exports were worth 72 million dollars, find the value of
        (i) minerals,
        (ii) agricultural produce exported.

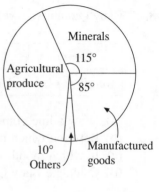

14. The pie chart shows how 120 boys go to school.
    (a) If 57 boys go to school by bus, calculate the value of x.
    (b) Find the number of boys who walk to school.
    (c) Find the ratio $\dfrac{\text{number of boys who walk to school}}{\text{number of boys who go to school by car}}$.
    (d) Find the percentage of the boys who go to school by car.

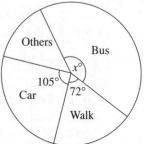

15. The pie chart represents the food intake of a boy on a particular day. He ate 1.8 kg of food on that day.
    (a) Find the percentage of carbohydrates in his intake, expressing your answer as a fraction in its lowest terms.
    (b) Find the value of the ratio
        $$\dfrac{\text{the weight of meat eaten}}{\text{the weight of the vegetables and fruits eaten}}.$$
    (c) Find the weight of the following types of food in his intake:
        (i) carbohydrates,
        (ii) vegetables,
        (iii) fruits.

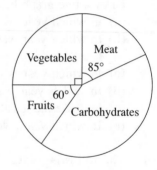

16. The pie chart shows the cost breakdown of a holiday.
    (a) Find what percentage of the cost was spent on
        (i) food,
        (ii) hotel.
    (b) Given that 15% of the total cost was spent on travel, find x.

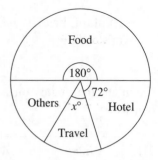

17. A company employs 720 people in four departments as shown in the table below:

Department	Marketing	Production	Administration	Research
Number employed	148	224	232	116

Draw a pie chart to illustrate the information.

18. The contents of 114 boxes of screws are examined. The diagram shows a histogram for the number of defective screws in each box.

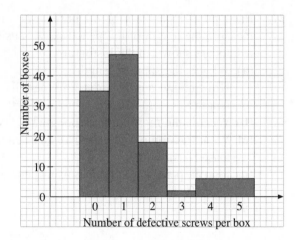

   (a) How many boxes contain no defective screw?
   (b) What is the most common number of defective screws per box?
   (c) How many boxes contain at least 2 defective screws?
   (d) Calculate the fraction of boxes containing less than 4 defective screws per box.

19. Each of the 600 boys in *Aces Sports Club* was asked to name his favourite sport. Their choices are given in the table below.

Sport	Badminton	Basketball	Athletics	Soccer	Tennis
Number of boys	70	90	105	205	130

   Represent the results using a pie chart.

20. The marks out of ten scored by a class in a test are given in the following table:

Marks	6	7	8	9	10
Number of students	2	5	10	12	6

   (a) How many pupils sat for the test?
   (b) Find the percentage of students who scored more than 8 marks.

21. At a telephone exchange, the number of calls received in a minute interval was recorded for each of one hundred chosen intervals.
   The results are illustrated by the histogram.

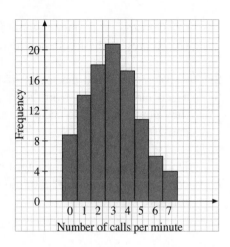

   (a) What is the most common number of calls per interval?
   (b) In how many intervals were 2 calls received per minute?
   (c) What fraction of the intervals chosen were there more than 3 calls per minute?
   (d) What percentage of the intervals were there not more than 3 calls per minute?

22. Each pupil in a class of 40 pupils was asked to measure the length of the pencil he was using. The results are shown in the histogram.

(a) What is the shortest length?
How many pupils are using pencils of this length?

(b) What is the most common length?

(c) What fraction of the class is using pencils of at least 11 cm long?

(d) Find the percentage of pupils using pencils shorter than 10 cm.

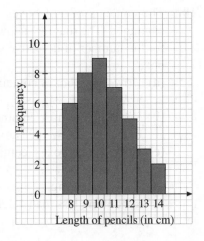

23. A gardener sowed 5 seeds into each of 100 plant pots. The number of seeds germinating in each pot was recorded and the results given in the table below:

Number of seeds germinating	0	1	2	3	4	5
Number of pots	10	30	25	20	10	5

(a) Draw a histogram to show the results.

(b) How many seeds did the gardener sow altogether?

(c) What fraction of the seeds was germinating?

24. Thirty pupils were asked how many foreign countries they had visited. The answers are given below:

1	0	0	2	3	1	1	0	2	4
5	1	2	0	2	0	1	3	2	4
3	0	1	1	2	3	2	1	0	1

(a) Construct a frequency table for the above results.

(b) Represent the frequency distribution using a histogram.

25. A bakery reported that sales of its signature bread have doubled from 2004 to 2006 and they put up a chart to show the sales of 2004 and 2006.

Do you think that the diagram is a good comparison of the sales? Explain how you can improve the chart.

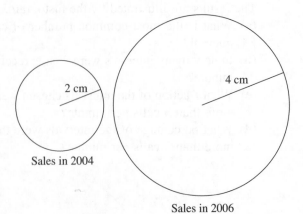

Real-life Performance Task: CCA Survey

You are the leader of the student council in your school. You have received complaints from your fellow schoolmates about the lack of co-curricular activities (CCA) in the school and if you do not do anything about it, they vow to overthrow you in the next election. Hence, in order to safeguard your position, you have decided to conduct a survey on the type of CCA they would like to have in the school. The survey has to be conducted on 30 students from your own level but you cannot choose all the students from your own class. After that, present the data collected using a table and an appropriate statistical graph. You can use *Microsoft Excel* to draw the statistical graph (see IT Worksheet on Statistical Diagrams on page 115). Write a brief report that shows the table of data and the statistical graph to the principal to explain the results of the survey and to put in some recommendations of CCA for the school.

Scoring Rubric

Competency Level	Conceptual Understanding	Mathematical Communication
4	• Competent in data collection • Accurate and appropriate table and statistical graph presented	• Excellent use of evidence to support recommendation
3	• Competent in data collection • Nearly accurate and appropriate table and statistical graph presented	• Good use of evidence to support recommendation
2	• Not so competent in data collection • Accurate but inappropriate table and statistical graph presented	• Weak use of evidence to support recommendation
1	• Not competent in data collection • Inaccurate and inappropriate table and statistical graph presented	• Did not make use of evidence to support recommendation
0	• No evidence of data collection • No evidence of table and statistical graph presented	• No evidence to support recommendation
Score		

Final Score:

[ ] / 8

Final Score	7–8	6	4–5	3	0–2
Grade	A	B	C	D	F

Teacher's Comments (if any):

_____

_____

You can use a computer software called Excel to draw the statistical graph for the *Real-life Performance Task: CCA Survey* on page 113. Excel is free as most computers are installed with Microsoft Office. Alternatively, use another free spreadsheet.

Section A: How to Enter Data

(a) Open an Excel Workbook.

(b) Enter in Cell A3: CCA

(c) Enter in Cell A4 onwards all the CCA preferred by the 30 students

(d) Enter in Cell B3: Number of Students

(e) Enter in Cell B4 onwards the number of students who prefer each of these CCA. It should look like the *sample* below:

CCA	Number of Students
Soccer	5
Basketball	3
NPCC	6
NCC	4
Scouts	8
Maths Club	4

To check whether you have entered the numbers correctly, you can sum up these numbers to see if they add up to 30 (the total number of students in this survey):

(f) Enter in Cell B10 (or the cell in the second column after the last row of data): =SUM(B4:B9)

(g) Press [Enter]. This will sum up all the numbers from the Cell B4 to the Cell B9. It should look like the *sample* below:

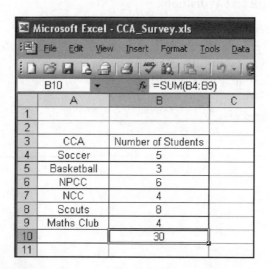

Section B: How to Enter Statistical Diagrams

(h) Select the table of values (including the heading row but excluding the sum). In the above *sample*, it means selecting Cells A3:B9.

(i) Select from the Toolbar: ***Insert ▸ Charts…***

(j) Choose the tab *Standard Charts* and then chart type *Column*. Select the first chart sub-type.

(k) Click *Next*, and then *Next* again.

(l) Choose the tab *Titles* and type under:
Chart title:	CCA Survey
Category (X) axis:	CCA
Value (Y) axis:	Number of Students

(m) Choose the tab *Legend* and **uncheck** the option ***Show Legend***.

(n) Click *Next*, and then *Finish*. It should look like the *sample* below:

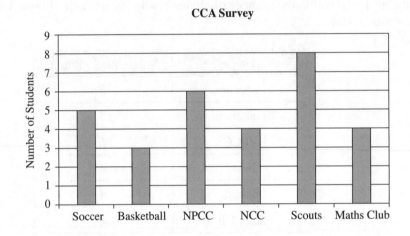

(o) You can click on the chart to move it and you can also resize the chart area.

(p) Click on the chart. Choose from the Toolbar: ***Chart ▸ Chart Type…***

(q) Under the tab *Standard Charts*, choose different chart types such as ***Bar**, **Line and Pie***. You can click the button ***Press and Hold to View Sample***.

(r) Click ***OK*** when you are done.

Section C: How to Print Excel Workbook

(s) Choose from the Toolbar: ***File ▸ Page Setup…***

(t) Under the tab *Page*, choose the *Scaling* option: ***Fit to 1 page wide by 1 page tall***. Click ***OK***. This will fit the table of values and the chart to one page.

(u) Choose from the Toolbar: ***File ▸ Print…***

(v) Click ***OK*** to print.

(w) Submit to teacher if necessary.

Term III Revision Test   Time: $1\frac{1}{2}$ h

1. The driver of a car travelling at 60 km/h is 80 km behind the driver of another car travelling at 50 km/h. How long will it take the faster car to catch up with the slower car? **[3]**

2. (a) If 60% of a number is equal to 84, find the number.
   (b) A man bought 200 mangoes for $60. He found that 10% of them were spoilt and sold the rest at 36 cents each. Find his profit. **[4]**

3. A motorist uses 1 litre of petrol for every 10.4 km travelled. Given that petrol costs $1.86 per litre, calculate the cost of petrol for a journey of 135.2 km. **[3]**

4. The mass of a truck and its load of cargo is 7.84 tons. What is the mass of the cargo, in kilograms, if the mass of the empty truck is 2.995 tons? **[2]**

5. (a) 12 men take 5 days to build a road 200 m long. How many days will 20 men take to build a road 400 m long? **[3]**
   (b) The radius of a circle is increased by 20%. Find the percentage change in the perimeter and area of the circle. **[3]**

6. The numbers of cars, motorcycles and lorries in a car park is represented in the given pie chart.
   (a) Calculate the value of x.
   (b) Given that there are 153 cars in the car park, calculate the number of motorcycles in the car park. **[3]**

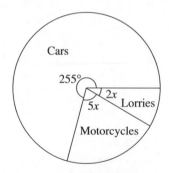

7. A motorist travels a distance of 154 km in $2\frac{3}{4}$ hours. Find, in km/h, his average speed for the journey. Find also his maximum speed during the journey given that it exceeds his average speed by 75%. If during the whole of the journey he only travels at this maximum speed for half an hour, find his average speed for the rest of his journey. **[4]**

8. The vertices of $\triangle ABC$ are $A(1, 2)$, $B(5, 10)$ and $C(9, 6)$. Find the gradients of the line
   (a) AB (b) AC (c) BC. **[3]**

9. The pupils in a school were asked to choose their favourite form of entertainment from television, cinema, radio and net surfing. Their replies are represented in the pie chart on the right.
   (a) Calculate the value of x.
   (b) If 330 pupils chose radio, find the total number of pupils in the school.
   (c) Find the percentage of pupils who chose cinema. **[4]**

10. A passenger train leaves Town A at 10 40 and travels at 80 km/h to Town B, arriving there at 13 25. Find the distance between Town A and Town B. **[3]**

11. (a) A garrison of 500 men has enough rations to last them 66 days. If they are reinforced by 50 men, how many days will the same rations last now? **[3]**
    (b) A new computer is priced at $3000. One shop sells it at an 18% discount, another sells it at a reduction of $500. Find the difference between the two prices. **[3]**

12. A cylindrical piece of cake of radius 14 cm and thickness 8 cm stands on a horizontal table. $\frac{1}{4}$ of the cake is removed by cutting vertically downwards through the radii OA and OB as shown in the diagram.

Find
(a) the volume of the remaining cake. **[3]**
(b) the total surface area of the remaining cake. **[5]**

$$\left(\text{Take } \pi = \frac{22}{7}\right)$$

13. (a) A new car cost $64 000. After one year its value depreciated by 20%. Find its value at the end of the first year. **[2]**
(b) A man saves 20% of his income. What is his income if he spends $1360 a month? **[2]**

14. A driver covers 180 km in 2 h 30 min. If he is driving at a constant speed, find the distance he covers in 5 minutes. **[3]**

15. A worker was paid $2.25 an hour and if he worked overtime, he was paid $3.50 an hour. If the worker received $127 for 52 hours of work, how many hours of overtime work did he do? **[4]**

Chapter 14

Basic Geometrical Concepts and Properties

 **Summary**

1. The **sum of all the angles** at a point is 360°.

2. The **sum of adjacent angles** on a straight line is 180°.

3. Fig. 14.1 shows two parallel lines, *AB* and *CD*, with a transversal *PQ*.
   (a) *x* and *y* are **vertically opposite angles** and are equal in size.
   (b) *x* and *q* are **corresponding angles** and are equal in size.
   (c) *e* and *b* are **alternate angles** and are equal in size.
   (d) *e* and *y* are **interior angles** and their sum is equal to 180°.

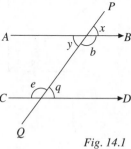

Fig. 14.1

 **Practice Questions**

Calculate the value of *x* and of *y* in the following figures.

1.

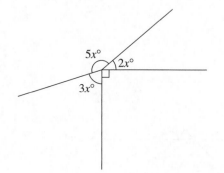

2.

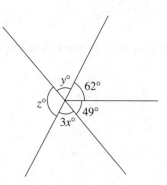

3.

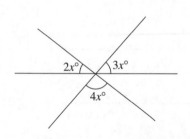

4.

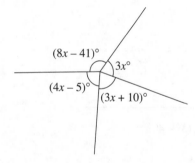

5.

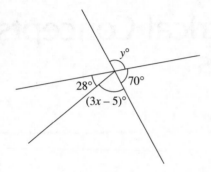

6.

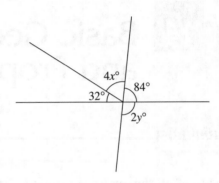

Calculate the value of x in each of the following figures.

7.

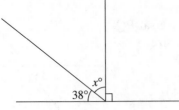

8.

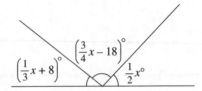

9.

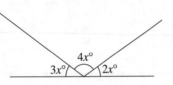

10.

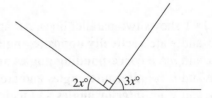

11.

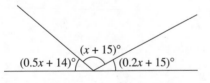

Find the value of x in each of the following figures.

12.

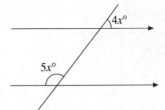

13.

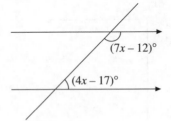

14.

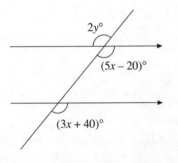

15.

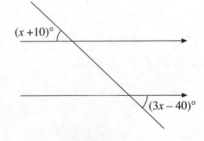

16.

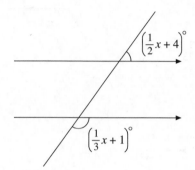

Calculate the value of x in each of the following figures.

17.

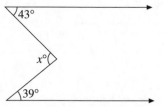

18.

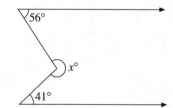

19.

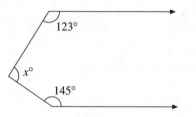

20.

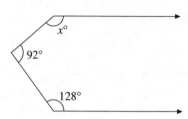

21.

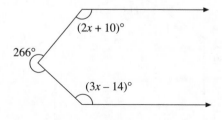

Calculate the value of the unknowns in the following figures.

22.

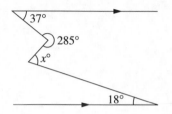

23.

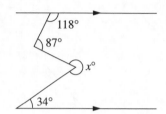

24.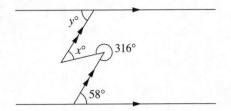

25.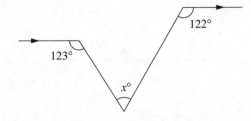

26.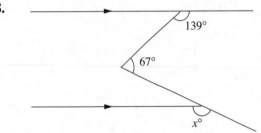

27.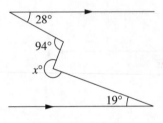

28.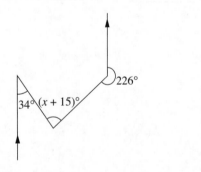

29.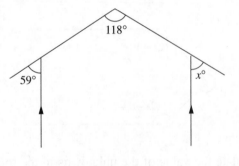

30.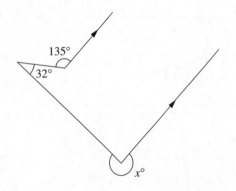

31.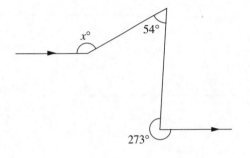

32.

33. In the diagram, *RS* // *PAQ*, *CD* // *ASB*, *AD̂C* = 62° and *QÂD* = 26°. Calculate
  (a) *x*
  (b) *y*

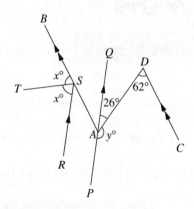

34. In the diagram, *PC* // *DF*, *AB* // *DE*, *ED̂F* = 84°, *QB̂D* = 74° and *PĈD* = 148°. Calculate
  (a) *AB̂Q*
  (b) *CD̂E*

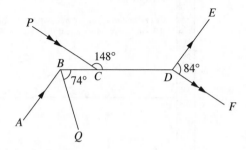

35. In the diagram, *RS* // *PBQ* // *CD*, *AB̂R* = 47° and *BĈD* = 86°. Calculate
  (a) *PB̂C*
  (b) *BR̂S*

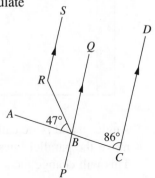

36. In the diagram, *AB* // *CD*, *BT* // *AD*, *XB̂T* = 68° and *XD̂C* = 58°. Calculate
  (a) *AX̂B*
  (b) *AB̂X*

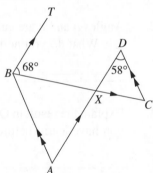

IT Worksheet: Corresponding Angles, Alternate Angles and Interior Angles

You need the Geometer's Sketchpad (GSP), a dynamic geometry software, to view and interact with the GSP template for this worksheet. If your school does not have a licensed copy of version 4, you may download the free evaluation version from www.keypress.com for trial first.

Open the appropriate template from the Workbook CD.

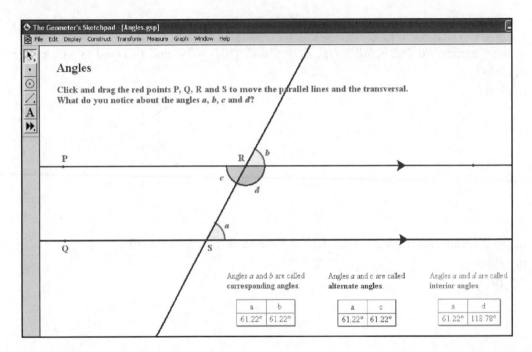

1. Angles *a* and *b* are called ***corresponding angles***. Click and drag the red points *P*, *Q*, *R* and *S* to move the parallel lines and the transversal (a transversal is a line that cuts two parallel lines). This will change the sizes of $\angle a$ and $\angle b$. What do you notice about the sizes of $\angle a$ and $\angle b$?

    [1]

2. Angles *a* and *c* are called ***alternate angles***. Repeat the above step to change the sizes of $\angle a$ and $\angle c$. What do you notice about the sizes of $\angle a$ and $\angle c$? **[1]**

3. Explain the result in Q2. ***Hint:*** Make use of $\angle b$, the result in Q1 and another angle property which you have learnt before. **[2]**

4. Angles *a* and *d* are called **interior angles**. Repeat the above step to change the sizes of angles *a* and *d*. What do you notice about the sizes of angles *a* and *d*? **Hint:** Consider the sum. **[1]**

_____

5. Explain the result in Q4. **Hint:** Make use of $\angle b$, the result in Q1 and another angle property which you have learnt before. **[2]**

_____

Summary

6. Summarise the three angle properties that you have learnt in this worksheet: **[1]**

(a) $\angle a = \angle$ _____ (corr. $\angle$s)

(b) $\angle a = \angle$ _____ (alt. $\angle$s)

(c) $\angle a + \angle d =$ _____ (int. $\angle$s)

How to Remember?

Just remember *F*, *Z* and *C*.

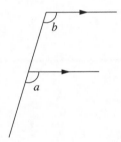 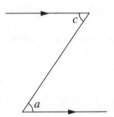 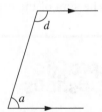

The letter *F* above is made up of one *r* above another *r*, and the phrase 'co*rr*esponding angles' has *rr*.

The angles in the letter *Z* above have the sense of being *alternate* to each other. So they are *alternate* angles.

The angles above have the sense of being *inside* the letter *C*. So they are *interior* angles.

Final Score:

 / 8

Final Score	7–8	6	4–5	3	0–2
Grade	A	B	C	D	F

Teacher's Comments (if any):

_____

_____

Angle Properties of Polygons

Summary

1. The **sum of the angles of a triangle** is 180°.
    The **exterior angle** of a triangle is equal to the **sum of the interior opposite angles**.

2. A quadrilateral is a 4-sided plane figure. The sum of the angles of a quadrilateral is equal to 360°.
    *   The diagonals of a parallelogram bisect each other.
    *   The diagonals of a rectangle are equal in length and they bisect each other.
    *   The diagonals of a rhombus bisect each other at right angles.
    *   The diagonals of a square are equal in length and they bisect each other at right angles.
    *   The longer diagonal of a kite bisect the shorter diagonal at right angles.

3. The sum of the interior angles of an n-sided polygon is given by $(n - 2) \times 180°$ or $(2n - 4)$ right angles.

4. The sum of the exterior angles of an n-sided polygon is equal to 360°.

Practice Questions

Calculate the value of x and of y in the following figures.

1.

2.
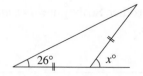

3.
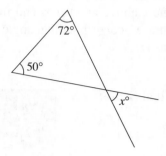

4.
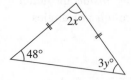

5.

Calculate the value of the unknowns in the following figures.

6.

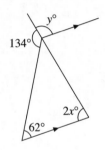

134°

$y°$

$2x°$

62°

7.

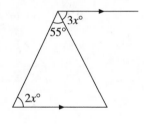

$3x°$

55°

$2x°$

8.

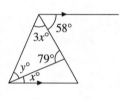

58°

$3x°$

79°

$y°$

$x°$

9.

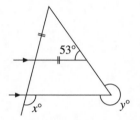

$x°$

$x°$

63°

10.

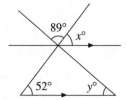

89°

$x°$

52°

$y°$

11.

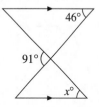

46°

91°

$x°$

12.

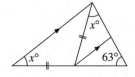

53°

$x°$

$y°$

13.

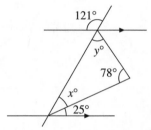

121°

$y°$

78°

$x°$

25°

14.

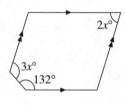

$2x°$

$3x°$

132°

15.

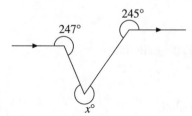

247°

245°

$x°$

Calculate the value of x and of y in the following rectangles.

16.

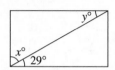

$y°$

$x°$

29°

17.

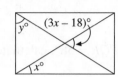

$y°$

$(3x - 18)°$

$x°$

Calculate the value of x and of y in the following kites.

18.
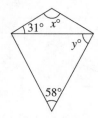

19.
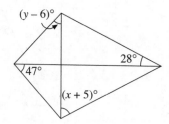

Calculate the value of x and of y in the following parallelograms.

20.
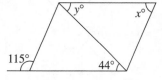

21.
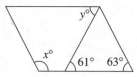

Calculate the value of x and of y in the following rhombuses.

22.
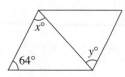

23.

24. In a rectangle $ABCD$, $A\hat{C}B = 55°$. Calculate
    (a) $A\hat{C}B$,   **(b)** $C\hat{A}B$.

25. In a rectangle $PQRS$, X is the midpoint of PQ and $S\hat{X}R = 110°$, calculate
    (a) $P\hat{S}X$,   **(b)** $X\hat{R}S$.

26. In a parallelogram $ABCD$, $B\hat{A}C = 56°$ and $B\hat{C}D = 70°$, calculate
    (a) $C\hat{B}A$,   **(b)** $A\hat{C}B$.

27. In a parallelogram $PQRS$, $Q\hat{P}S = 108°$, $R\hat{Q}S = 40°$, calculate
    (a) $P\hat{S}Q$,   **(b)** $Q\hat{S}R$.

28. In a rhombus $PQRS$, $P\hat{Q}R = 58°$, calculate
    (a) $Q\hat{R}S$,   **(b)** $Q\hat{P}R$.

29. In a rhombus $ABCD$, $A\hat{B}C = 114°$, calculate
    (a) $A\hat{B}D$,   **(b)** $A\hat{C}D$.

30. In a kite $ABCD$, $AB = BC$, $AD = CD$, $A\hat{D}C = 66°$ and $B\hat{A}C = 42°$, calculate
    (a) $A\hat{C}D$,   **(b)** $A\hat{B}C$.

31. In a kite $PQRS$, $PQ = PS$, $QR = RS$, $P\hat{Q}R = 118°$ and $Q\hat{R}S = 72°$, calculate
   (a) $R\hat{S}Q$,
   (b) $Q\hat{P}S$.

32. In a trapezium $ABCD$, AB is parallel to DC, $AB = AD$, $A\hat{D}C = 64°$ and $B\hat{C}D = 54°$, calculate
   (a) $A\hat{B}D$,
   (b) $D\hat{B}C$.

33. In a trapezium $PQRS$, PQ is parallel to SR, $PQ = PS = QR$ and $P\hat{S}R = 66°$, calculate
   (a) $Q\hat{R}S$,
   (b) $P\hat{Q}S$.

34. In the diagram, $ABCD$ is a square, $BA = BQ$, QPC and BPD are straight lines and $P\hat{B}Q = 21°$. Calculate
   (a) $B\hat{A}Q$
   (b) $D\hat{C}Q$
   (c) $Q\hat{P}B$

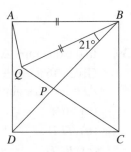

35. In the diagram, CDP is a straight line, $\triangle AQD$ is equilateral, $B\hat{A}R = 90°$, $Q\hat{A}R = 135°$, $B\hat{C}D = 106°$ and $A\hat{B}C = 100°$. Calculate
   (a) $B\hat{A}D$
   (b) $C\hat{D}A$
   (c) $P\hat{D}Q$

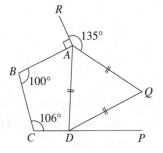

36. In the diagram, $ABCD$ is a rhombus, ADR is an equilateral triangle, $APQR$ is a straight line and $\angle APD = 90°$, $A\hat{C}B = 68°$. Calculate
   (a) $A\hat{B}C$
   (b) $P\hat{D}Q$
   (c) $D\hat{Q}R$

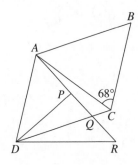

37. In the diagram, $ABCD$ is a rhombus, $B\hat{A}C = 33°$, $D\hat{C}R = 72°$ and $B\hat{Q}R = 52°$. Calculate
   (a) $Q\hat{B}C$
   (b) $B\hat{D}C$
   (c) the reflex angle $B\hat{C}R$

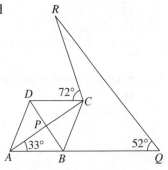

38. In the diagram, *ACDE* is a trapezium with *AC* // *ED*. Given that
$E\hat{A}B = 52°$, $C\hat{D}R = 126°$, $P\hat{B}C = 90°$ and *EQ* // *DR*. Calculate
   (a) $P\hat{E}Q$
   (b) $B\hat{C}D$
   (c) $E\hat{D}R$

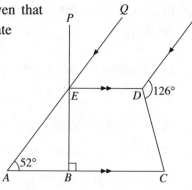

39. In the diagram, △*ABE* is an isosceles triangle and *BCDE* is a rhombus.
Given that $B\hat{D}E = 61°$, $B\hat{T}E = 81°$, *AB* = *BE* and both *ABC* and
ATE are straight lines. Calculate
   (a) $A\hat{B}T$
   (b) $T\hat{E}D$
   (c) $B\hat{C}D$

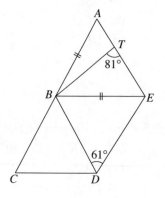

40. In the diagram, *ABCD* is a parallelogram, *AD* = *AE*, *BAE* is a straight
line, $A\hat{B}C = 88°$, $E\hat{A}F = 162°$ and $A\hat{F}C = 48°$. Calculate
   (a) $A\hat{E}D$
   (b) $F\hat{A}D$
   (c) $B\hat{C}F$

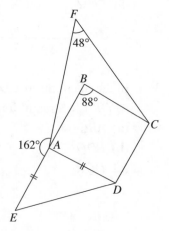

41. Calculate the sum of the interior angles of a polygon with
   (a) 7 sides,   **(b)** 17 sides,
   (c) 22 sides,   **(d)** 30 sides,
giving your answers in terms of the number of right angles.

42. Find the number of sides of a polygon if the sum of its interior angles is
   (a) 16,   **(b)** 26,
   (c) 42,   **(d)** 70 right angles.

43. Find the number of sides of a regular polygon whose interior angle is
    (a) 90°,   (b) 108°,
    (c) 156°,   (d) 165.6°.

44. Calculate the size of each interior angle of a regular polygon with
    (a) 30 sides,   (b) 16 sides,
    (c) 14 sides,   (d) 11 sides.

45. In a quadrilateral $ABCD$, the interior angles marked A, B, C and D are in the ratio $6 : 7 : 8 : 9$. Calculate the greatest interior angle and the greatest exterior angle.

46. $ABCDEF$ is a regular hexagon, calculate
    (a) $A\hat{B}C$,   (b) $A\hat{C}D$,   (c) $C\hat{A}E$.

47. The points A, B, C and D are consecutive vertices of a regular polygon which has 12 sides. Calculate
    (a) $A\hat{B}C$,   (b) $A\hat{C}D$.

48. $ABCDE$ is a regular pentagon. AB and DC are produced to meet at T, calculate $B\hat{T}C$.

49. The exterior angles of a triangle are $(2x + 10)°$, $(3x - 5)°$ and $(2x + 40)°$. Calculate
    (a) x,
    (b) the smallest interior angle,
    (c) the largest interior angle.

50. The sum of the interior angles of a polygon is twice the sum of its exterior angles. Find the number of sides of the polygon.

51. One of the interior angles of a polygon with n sides is $124°$ whereas the other $(n - 1)$ angles are each equal to $142°$. Find the value of n.

52. Given that the interior angles of a quadrilateral are $(2x + 15)°$, $(2x - 5)°$, $(3x + 75)°$ and $(3x - 25)°$. Calculate
    (a) x,
    (b) the smallest interior angle,
    (c) the smallest exterior angle.

53. One of the interior angles of a polygon is $95°$ and the rest are each equal to $169°$. Find the number of sides of the polygon.

54. One of the interior angles of a polygon is $172°$ and the rest are each equal to $158°$. Find the number of sides of the polygon.

55. The interior angles of a hexagon are $(2x + 17)°$, $(3x - 25)°$, $(2x + 49)°$, $(x + 40)°$, $(4x - 17)°$ and $(3x - 4)°$. Calculate
    (a) x,
    (b) the smallest interior angle,
    (c) the smallest exterior angle.

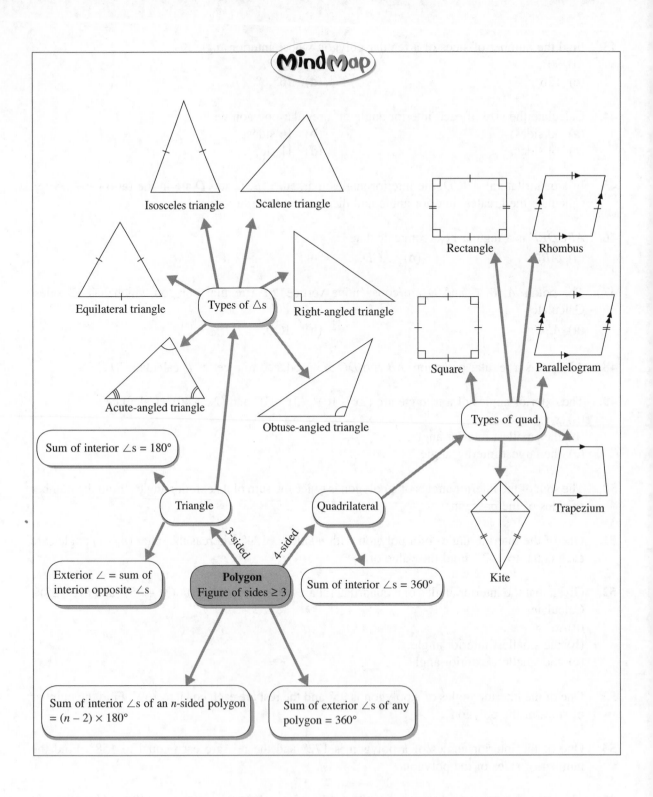

Isosceles triangle

Scalene triangle

Rectangle

Rhombus

Equilateral triangle

Types of △s

Right-angled triangle

Square

Parallelogram

Acute-angled triangle

Obtuse-angled triangle

Types of quad.

Trapezium

Sum of interior ∠s = 180°

Triangle

Quadrilateral

Kite

Exterior ∠ = sum of interior opposite ∠s

3-sided

4-sided

Polygon
Figure of sides ≥ 3

Sum of interior ∠s = 360°

Sum of interior ∠s of an *n*-sided polygon = $(n - 2) \times 180°$

Sum of exterior ∠s of any polygon = 360°

Poem, Rap or Song: Angles and Polygons

This assessment covers *Chapter 14: Basic Geometrical Concepts* and *Properties* as well.

The Dead Poet's Society is recruiting members. You are to submit a poem, rap or song based on the theme ***Angles and Polygons*** in order to enrol as a member. The chairman of the Dead Poet's Society, Mr J. B. B. Token, has kindly provided a sample for you as shown below as a reference.

The poem, rap or song submitted should be at least 2 stanzas of 4 lines each. You should include some key mathematical terms of the topics in your poem (for example, alternate angles, exterior angles, angle sum of triangle, hexagon). Let your creative juices flow!

Sample: A Rap on Angles and Polygons

There's the equilateral triangle
In which all sides have the same angle
Not to forget the isosceles triangle
In which 2 out of 3 angles are equal

Scalene of course, all sides differing
Like us, some plump and others thin
But who can forget, the cutest one of all
With acute angles forming it, they all extol

Scoring Rubric

Competency Level	Conceptual Understanding	Creativity	Mathematical Communication
4	• Made use of mathematical concepts accurately and comprehensively	• Had shown excellent imagination and a lot of original ideas	• Poem/rap/song had a natural flow and rhythm with excellent choice of words
3	• Made use of mathematical concepts accurately but not comprehensively	• Had shown good imagination and some original ideas	• Poem/rap/song had a nearly natural flow and rhythm with good choice of words
2	• Made use of mathematical concepts but with minor errors	• Had shown some imagination and some interesting ideas	• Poem/rap/song had some flow and rhythm but a mediocre choice of words
1	• Made use of mathematical concepts but with major errors	• Lacked imagination and work was not original	• Poem/rap/song had no natural flow and rhythm and a mediocre choice of words
0	• No evidence of mathematical concepts	• Irrelevant piece of work	• Poem/rap/song had no flow and rhythm and bad choice of words
Score			

Final Score:

☐ / 12

Final Score	10–12	8–9	6–7	4–5	0–3
Grade	A	B	C	D	F

Teacher's Comments (if any):

_____

_____

If you do not have a computer, you can skip Section A.

Section A: Exploration with IT

You need the Geometer's Sketchpad (GSP), a dynamic geometry software, to view and interact with the GSP template for this worksheet. If your school does not have a licensed copy of version 4, you may download the free evaluation version from www.keypress.com for trial first.

Open the appropriate template from the Workbook CD.

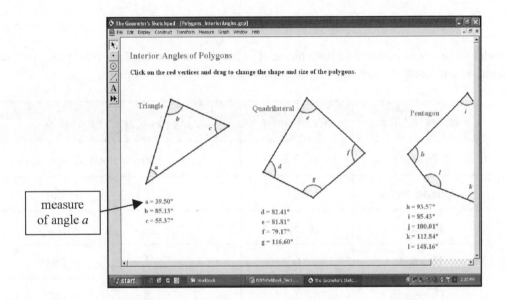

1. Click on the red vertices and drag to change the shape and size of the polygons. What do you notice about the sizes of the interior angles of the polygons? **[1]**

_____

To calculate the sum of all the interior angles of the triangle, do the following:
- **(a)** Choose from the Toolbar: *Measure ▶ Calculate…* A calculator will appear.
- **(b)** Click on the *measure of angle a* (see diagram above). It will appear in the calculator.
- **(c)** Click on the **+** button in the calculator.
- **(d)** Click on the *measure of angle b*. Then click on the **+** button in the calculator.
- **(e)** Click on the *measure of angle c*. Then click *OK* in the calculator.

2. What is the sum of the interior angles of the triangle? **[1]**

_____

3. Click on the red vertices and drag to change the shape and size of the triangle. What do you notice about the sum of the interior angles of the triangle? **[1]**

_____

4. Repeat the above steps to calculate the sum of all the interior angles of the quadrilateral. What is the sum of the interior angles of the quadrilateral? **[1]**

_____

5. Click on the red vertices and drag to change the shape and size of the quadrilateral. What do you notice about the sum of the interior angles of the quadrilateral? **[1]**

_____

6. Repeat the above steps to calculate the sum of all the interior angles of the pentagon, hexagon, heptagon and octagon, and record your observations in the table below. **[3]**

Name of Polygon	No. of Sides	Sum of Interior Angles
Triangle	3	$180° = 1 \times 180°$
Quadrilateral	4	_____° = _____ × 180°
Pentagon	5	_____° = _____ × 180°
Hexagon	6	_____° = _____ × 180°
Heptagon	7	_____° = _____ × 180°
Octagon	8	_____° = _____ × 180°

7. Compare the last two columns of the table above. What is the formula for the sum of the interior angles of an n-sided polygon or an n-gon? **[1]**

_____

Section B tells you why the formula works.

Section B: Exploration without IT

Recap

8. What is the sum of the interior angles of a triangle? **Ans:** _____ **[1]**

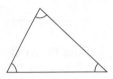

Exploration

9. Any quadrilateral can be divided into 2 triangles as shown on the right. What is the sum of the interior angles of a quadrilateral? **[1]**

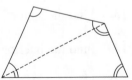

_____

10. Complete the table below by dividing the polygon into triangles. **[3]**

Name of Polygon	No. of Sides	Polygon	No. of Triangles	Sum of Interior Angles
Triangle	3		1	$1 \times 180° = 180°$
Quadrilateral	4		2	$2 \times 180° =$
Pentagon	5			
Hexagon	6			
Heptagon	7			
Octagon	8			

New Syllabus Mathematics Workbook 1

11. Compare the last two columns of the table above. What is the formula for the sum of the interior angles of an *n*-sided polygon or an *n*-gon? **[1]**

_____

Section C: Application

12. Find the sum of the interior angles of a 10-sided polygon.   Ans: _____ **[1]**

13. Find the sum of the interior angles of a 12-sided polygon.   Ans: _____ **[1]**

14. Find the interior angle of a **regular** 9-sided polygon.   Ans: _____ **[1]**

Section D: Extension

15. Does the formula in Q7 and Q11 apply for concave polygons (see below)? Investigate. You can use the IT method in Section A or the non-IT method in Section B. **[1]**

_____

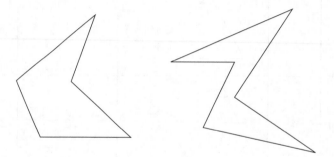

Conclusion

16. Write down one main lesson that you have learnt from this worksheet. **[1]**

_____

Final Score:

[   ] **/ 20**

Final Score	16–20	13–15	10–12	7–9	0–6
Grade	A	B	C	D	F

Teacher's Comments (if any):

_____

_____

IT Worksheet: Exterior Angles of Polygons

You need the Geometer's Sketchpad (GSP), a dynamic geometry software, to view and interact with the GSP template for this worksheet. If your school does not have a licensed copy of version 4, you may download the free evaluation version from www.keypress.com for trial first.

Open the appropriate template from the Workbook CD.

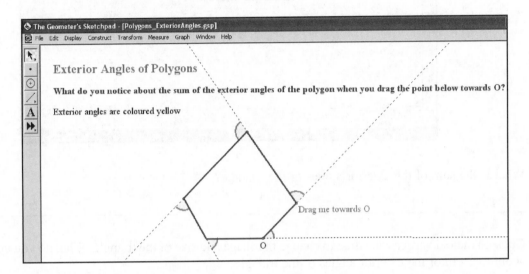

1. Click and drag the point "Drag me towards *O*". What do you notice about the sum of the exterior angles of the polygon?   **[1]**

_____

But does it work for all polygons?

2. Click on the tab *Triangle* at the bottom left hand corner to get the template below. Click on the red vertices and drag to change the shape and size of the triangle. What do you notice about the sizes of the exterior angles of the triangle?   **[1]**

_____

To calculate the sum of all the exterior angles of the triangle, do the following:
(a) Choose from the Toolbar: *Measure ▶ Calculate…* A calculator will appear.
(b) Click on the *measure of angle a* (see diagram below). It will appear in the calculator.
(c) Click on the **+** button in the calculator.
(d) Click on the *measure of angle b*. Then click on the **+** button in the calculator.
(e) Click on the *measure of angle c*. Then click *OK* in the calculator.

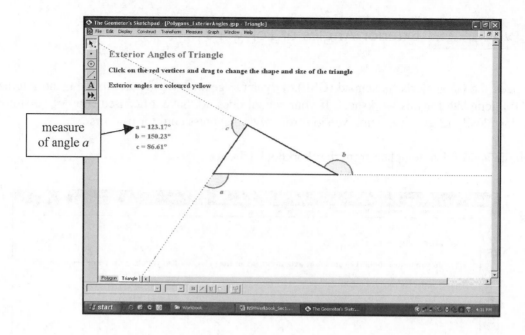

Exterior Angles of Triangle

Click on the red vertices and drag to change the shape and size of the triangle

Exterior angles are coloured yellow

measure of angle *a*

a = 123.17°
b = 150.23°
c = 86.61°

3. What is the sum of the exterior angles of the triangle?   [1]

    _____

4. Click on the red vertices and drag to change the shape and size of the triangle. What do you notice about the sum of the exterior angles of the triangle?   [1]

    _____

5. Click on the tab *Quadrilateral* at the bottom left hand corner. Repeat the above steps to calculate the sum of all the exterior angles of the quadrilateral. What do you notice about the sum of the exterior angles of the quadrilateral?   [1]

    _____

6. Repeat the above steps to calculate the sum of all the exterior angles of the pentagon and hexagon. What do you notice about the sum of the exterior angles of the pentagon and of the hexagon?   [1]

    _____

7. Does the sum of the exterior angles of an *n*-sided polygon depend on the number of sides, *n*, of the polygon?   [1]

    _____

8. State the sum of the exterior angles of any *n*-sided polygon.   [1]

    _____

Final Score:

	/ 8				

Final Score	7–8	6	4–5	3	0–2
Grade	A	B	C	D	F

Teacher's Comments (if any):

_____

_____

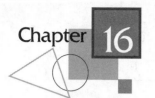

Chapter 16 Geometrical Constructions

- When constructing geometrical figures, use a sharp pencil to draw points and lines finely and clearly.

- All construction lines must be clearly shown and do not erase the construction lines that you have drawn.

1. Draw a line *AB* of length 8.4 cm. Construct the perpendicular bisector of *AB*.

2. Draw a line *PQ* of length 6 cm. Construct a line perpendicular to *PQ* and passing through the point *P*.

3. Draw an angle *PQR* of 88°. Construct the angle bisector of $P\hat{Q}R$.

4. Draw a line *PQ* of length 8 cm. Using a protractor, draw angles *PQR* and *QPR* such that $P\hat{Q}R = 58°$ and $Q\hat{P}R = 76°$. Measure $P\hat{R}Q$ and the lengths of *PR* and *QR*.

5. Draw a line *PQ* of length 9.6 cm. Construct the perpendicular bisector of *PQ* and angle *PQR* such that $P\hat{Q}R = 65°$ where *R* is the point on the perpendicular bisector of *PQ*. Measure the length of *PR* and of *QR*. Are they equal? Using your set square, construct a line parallel to *PQ* and passing through *R*.

6. Draw a line *AB* 8 cm long. Using a protractor, draw $A\hat{B}C = 64°$ and $B\hat{A}C = 46°$. Construct the angle bisectors of $A\hat{B}C$ and $B\hat{A}C$ and let the two angle bisectors meet at a point, *X*. Measure the length of *AX*.

7. Construction △*ABC* such that *AB* = 8.3 cm, *BC* = 7.9 cm and *AC* = 9.2 cm. Measure and write down the value of $A\hat{B}C$.

8. Construct △*PQR* such that *PQ* = 8.5 cm, *PR* = 4.6 cm and $Q\hat{P}R = 54°$. Measure and write down the length of *QR*.

9. Construct △*LMN* such that *LM* = 6.9 cm, $L\hat{M}N = 49°$ and $M\hat{L}N = 74°$. Measure and write down the length of *LN*.

10. Construct $\triangle XYZ$ such that $XY = 6.6$ cm, $XZ = 9.2$ cm and $X\hat{Y}Z = 98°$. Measure and write down the value of $Y\hat{X}Z$.

11. Construct an isosceles triangle PQR such that $PQ = PR = 7.2$ cm and $QR = 5$ cm. Measure and write down the value of $P\hat{Q}R$.

12. Construct an isosceles triangle ABC such that $AB = AC = 6.8$ cm and $A\hat{B}C = 54°$. Measure and write down the length of BC.

13. Construct $\triangle ABC$ such that $AB = 6$ cm, $BC = 7$ cm and $AC = 6.5$ cm. Construct the angle bisector of $A\hat{B}C$ and let this bisector cut AC at X. Measure and write down the length of BX.

14. Construct a rectangle whose sides are equal to 5 cm and 6.8 cm. Measure and write down the length of the diagonal.

15. Construct a parallelogram $PQRS$ where $PQ = 5.6$ cm, $PS = 4.5$ cm and $S\hat{P}Q = 72°$. Measure and write down the length of PR and of QS.

16. Construct a parallelogram $ABCD$ where $AB = 6.4$ cm, $AD = 7.6$ cm and $B\hat{A}D = 115°$. Measure and write down the length of BD and the value of $B\hat{D}A$.

17. Construct a rhombus of side 6.5 cm with one angle equals 56°. Measure and write down the length of the two diagonals.

18. Construct $\triangle ABC$ where $AB = 11.5$ cm, $AC = 10.8$ cm and $BC = 9.5$ cm. Measure and write down the size of $B\hat{A}C$ and $A\hat{B}C$.

19. Construct $\triangle PQR$ where $PQ = PR = 9.6$ cm and $QR = 12$ cm. Measure and write down the value of $P\hat{Q}R$.

20. Construct $\triangle ABC$ where $AB = 12.4$ cm, $BC = 6.4$ cm and $AC = 13.4$ cm. Measure and write down the value of $A\hat{B}C$. Construct the angle bisector of $A\hat{C}B$.

21. Construct $\triangle DEF$ in which $DE = 13$ cm, $EF = 5$ cm and $DF = 12$ cm. Construct the perpendicular bisector of DF and let it cut DE at G. Measure and write down the length of GF and the size of $E\hat{D}F$.

22. Construct $\triangle IJK$ where $IJ = 8$ cm, $I\hat{J}K = 55°$ and $JIK = 64°$. Measure and write down the length of IK and JK. Construct the perpendicular bisector JK and let it cut IJ at M. Measure and write down the length of IM.

23. Construct $\triangle DEF$ with $DE = 8.5$ cm, $DF = 9.2$ cm and $D\hat{E}F = 75°$. Measure and write down the length of EF.
    Construct the angle bisector of $E\hat{D}F$ and let it cut EF at G. Measure and write down the length of DG.

24. Construct a rectangle $ABCD$ where $AB = 9$ cm and $BC = 7.8$ cm. Measure and write down the length of BD and $A\hat{B}D$.

25. Construct a parallelogram $PQRS$ with $PQ = 10.3$ cm, $PS = 6.3$ cm and $P\hat{Q}R = 105°$. Measure and write down the lengths of the diagonals PR and QS.

26. Construct a rhombus $HKIJ$ where $HK = 7.2$ cm and $H\hat{K}I = 110°$. Measure and write down the lengths of the diagonals HI and KJ.

27. Construct a trapezium $DEFG$ where $DE = 10.8$ cm, $D\hat{E}F = 75°$, $G\hat{D}E = 85°$ and $DG = 7.4$ cm. Measure and write down the length of GE and GF.

28. Construct a square $ABCD$ with $BC = 8.2$ cm. Measure and write down the length of BD.

29. Construct a kite $PQRS$ where $PQ = QR = 3.6$ cm, $PS = 6.9$ cm and $P\hat{Q}R = 124°$. Measure and write down the lengths of the diagonals PR and QS.

30. Construct a rhombus $ABCD$ with $BC = 8.4$ cm and $A\hat{B}C = 75°$. Measure and write down the lengths of the diagonals AC and BD.

31. Construct a square $WXYZ$ where $WZ = 7.4$ cm. Measure and write down the length of the diagonal WY.

32. Construct a parallelogram $ABCD$ with $AB = 9.8$ cm, $AD = 7.2$ cm and $A\hat{B}C = 68°$. Measure and write down the lengths of the diagonal AC and BD.

33. Construct a rectangle $PQRS$ with $PQ = 10.4$ cm and $P\hat{Q}S = 32°$. Measure and write down the lengths of PS and PR.

34. Construct a trapezium $WXYZ$ with $WX = 11.9$ cm, $W\hat{X}Y = 90°$, $WY = 13.9$ cm and $YZ = 8.2$ cm. Measure and write down the length of WZ and the size of $X\hat{W}Z$.

35. Construct a kite $ABCD$ where $A\hat{B}C = 116°$, $AC = 6.4$ cm and $BD = 11.6$ cm. Measure and write down the lengths of AB and AD.

36. Construct $\triangle DEF$ with $DE = 8.5$ cm, $DF = 9.2$ cm and $D\hat{E}F = 75°$. Measure and write down the length of EF.

37. Construct a quadrilateral $ABCD$ where $BC = 6$ cm, $CD = 9$ cm, $AD = 6$ cm, $AB = 4.5$ cm and $BD = 4$ cm. Measure and write down the value of $A\hat{D}C$.

38. Construct a quadrilateral $ABCD$ where $AB = 8.5$ cm, $BC = 6.5$ cm, $A\hat{B}C = 110°$, $AD = 9.8$ cm and $C\hat{A}D = 42°$. Measure and write down the lengths of AC and CD.

39. Construct a quadrilateral $ABCD$ in which $AB = 5$ cm, $BC = 4.2$ cm, $AD = 5.4$ cm, $A\hat{B}C = 105°$ and $B\hat{A}D = 85°$. Measure and write down the length of CD.

40. Construct a quadrilateral *PQRS* in which *PQ* = 6.2 cm, *PR* = 8.2 cm, $Q\hat{P}R$ = 38°, *PS* = 7.2 cm and *SR* = 5 cm. Measure and write down the length of *SQ* and the value of $P\hat{R}S$.

41. Construct a trapezium *PQRS* in which *PQ* is parallel to *SR*, *PQ* = 4 cm, $S\hat{P}Q$ = 110°, *PS* = 5 cm and *SR* = 6.8 cm. Measure and write down the length of *QR* and the value of $P\hat{Q}R$.

42. Construct a quadrilateral *ABCD* in which *AB* = 7.6 cm, *AD* = 5.3 cm, $A\hat{B}C$ = 105°, $B\hat{A}D$ = 110° and $A\hat{D}C$ = 82°. Measure and write down the length of *CD* and of *BC*.

43. Construct a quadrilateral *PQRS* in which *PQ* = 6.2 cm, *PS* = 5.7 cm, *RS* = 4.8 cm, $Q\hat{P}S$ = 85° and $P\hat{S}R$ = 112°. Measure and write down the length of *QR* and of *QS*.

44. Construct a trapezium *ABCD* in which *AB* = 9.4 cm, *BC* = 5.2 cm, *CD* = 3.8 cm and $A\hat{B}C$ = 80°. Measure and write down the length of *AD* and the value of $B\hat{A}D$.

IT Worksheet: Construction Using Geometry Software

This worksheet should be done **after** you have learnt this topic on geometrical constructions using a pair of compasses. You need the Geometer's Sketchpad (GSP), a dynamic geometry software, to view and interact with the GSP template for this worksheet. If your school does not have a licensed copy of version 4, you many download the free evaluation version from www.keyprress.com for trial first.

Section A: Bisection of an Angle

Task 1: To construct the angle bisector of $A\hat{B}C$

Open the appropriate template from the Workbook CD.

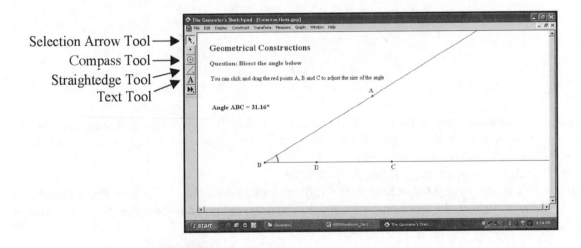

Recall how you bisect an angle by drawing some **arcs** using a pair of compasses. In GSP, you will use the *compass tool* to draw **full circles** instead of arcs.

(a)   Click on the ***Compass Tool*** on the Toolbox on the left (see above).

(b)   Click on Point *B* but do not release the left mouse button. Drag the pointer along the line *BC* and you will see a red point at the tip of the white arrow. Release the mouse button when the red dot is on Point *D*.

(c)   Click on the ***Selection Arrow Tool*** on the Toolbox (see above).

(d)   Click on the intersection between the circle and the line *AB*. A point will appear at the intersection.

(e)   Click on the ***Text Tool*** on the Toolbox (see above).

(f)   Click on the point in **(d)**. It will be labelled *E*. If the label is not *E*, double-click on the letter and change it to *E* under the tab *Label*. It should look like the diagram below.

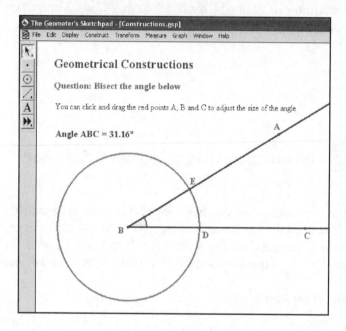

Note that drawing the circle above is similar to using a pair of compasses to draw two arcs to cut the two lines like this:

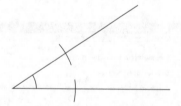

(g)   Click on the ***Compass Tool***. Click on Point *D* and drag to draw a circle. Release the left mouse button only when the red point at the tip of the white arrow is on the line *BC* between *D* and *C* (see diagram on the next page).

(h)   Label the red point in **(g)** *F* [see Steps (e)-(f)].

(i)   Click on the ***Straightedge Tool*** on the Toolbox (see first diagram). Click on Point *D* and drag to Point *F*. Release the left mouse button only when the red point at the tip of the white arrow is on Point *F* (see diagram on the next page).

(j) Click on the *Selection Arrow Tool*.

(k) Click on Point *E*. (Line segment *DF* should still be highlighted. If not, click on it.)

(l) Choose from the Toolbar: ***Construct ▶ Circle By Center+Radius***. This will construct a circle with the same radius as the circle in **(g)**.

(m) The two circles in **(g)** and **(l)** intersect at two points. Click on the intersection further away from Point *B*. A point will appear at this intersection. Label it *G* [see Steps (e)-(f)].

(n) Click and hold down on the *Straightedge Tool*. 3 more buttons will appear:

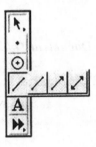

(o) Select the second button: ⬚

(p) Click on Point *B* and drag to draw a ray. Release the left mouse button only when the red point at the tip of the white arrow is on Point *G*.

The ray *BG* bisects the angle *ABC* as shown in the diagram below. It is called the angle bisector of ∠*ABC*.

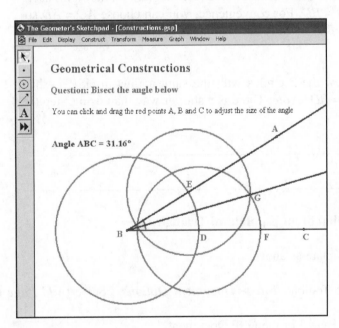

(q) Click on the *Selection Arrow Tool*. Then click on the 3 circles and the points *D*, *E* and *F*.

(r) Choose from the Toolbar: ***Display ▶ Hide Objects***.

(s) Click on the points *A*, *B* and *G* **in order**.

(t) Choose from the Toolbar: ***Measure ▶ Angle***. This will show the size of ∠*ABG*. The letter *m* stands for the *m*easure of the size of the angle.

(u) Click and move each of the points *A*, *B* and *G*. This will change the size of ∠*ABC*.

1. What do you notice about the relationship between $\angle ABC$ and $\angle ABG$? Why? **[1]**

_____

_____

Section B: Bisection of a Line Segment

Use the same GSP template as above.

(v) Choose from the Toolbar: *File ▸ Document Options...* Select *Add Page ▸ Blank Page*. Then click *OK*.
You are now on Page 2 of the GSP Document.

Task 2

Using what you have learnt above, draw a line segment *AB* and then construct the perpendicular bisector of the line segment in the same GSP template. Use the Hint and Question 2 below to help you. **[2]**

Hint
If you use a pair of compasses to construct the perpendicular bisector of a line segment, you need to draw the four arcs (see diagram on the right) such that $AC = BC$ and $AD = BD$. For convenience, you can choose $AC = AD$ so that $AC = BC = AD = BD$. In GSP, this will mean drawing 2 circles with the same radius.

2. How do you draw the 2 circles with the same radius in GSP so that $AC = BC = AD = BD$? *Note*: There is a shorter way than using Step (**l**) above. **[1]**

_____

_____

Section C: Construction of an Equilateral Triangle

Use the same GSP template as above.

(w) Choose from the Toolbar: *File ▸ Document Options...* Select *Add Page ▸ Blank Page*. Then click *OK*.
You are now on Page 3 of the GSP Document.

Task 3

Using what you have learnt in Section B, construct an equilateral triangle *ABC*. **Hint**: What do you notice about $\triangle ABC$ on Page 2 of your GPS Document?   [2]

3. Explain why the triangle that you have constructed on Page 3 of the GSP Document is equilateral.   [1]

_____

_____

Final Score:

| | / 10 |

Final Score	8–10	7	5–6	4	0–3
Grade	A	B	C	D	F

Teacher's Comments (if any):

_____

_____

Term IV Revision Test   Time: 1 h

1. Find the values of x, y and z in the figure below.

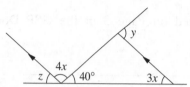

[6]

2. Construct $\triangle XYZ$, given that $XY = 69$ mm, $YZ = 57$ mm and $ZX = 48$ mm. If L, M and N are the midpoints of YZ, ZX and XY respectively, measure LM, MN and NL.   [4]

3. Construct $\triangle ABC$ in which $AB = 5$ cm, $BC = 10$ cm and $A\hat{B}C = 30°$. Construct, also, the perpendicular from C to BA produced to meet at point X.   [4]

4. Find the angles, marked x, y and z in the diagram.

[3]

5. (a) Find the size of each interior angle of a regular polygon with 45 sides.   [2]
   (b) The interior angles of a pentagon are $3x°$, $4x°$, $5x°$, $(3x° - 20°)$ and $(5x° - 50°)$. Find the value of x. Find also the largest interior angle and exterior angle.   [4]

6. Find the value of the unknown in each of the following diagrams:
   (a)   (b)

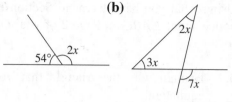

[4]

7. In the figure, HAK is parallel to BDE, $A\hat{D}E = 110°$, $A\hat{B}C = B\hat{A}C = 2x$, $C\hat{A}D = x$, $A\hat{C}D = y$ and $B\hat{A}H = z$. Calculate the values of x, y and z.   [6]

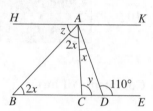

8. Construct a parallelogram $ABCD$ in which $AB = 9$ cm, $AD = 6$ cm and $B\hat{C}D = 55°$. On the same diagram, construct a perpendicular from D to AB and measure its length.   [4]

9. Two interior angles of a polygon are $88°$ and $99°$, and each of the rest equals to $163°$. Find the number of sides of the polygon.   [3]

End-of-Year Specimen Paper

*Answer **all** the questions.*   **Time: $2\frac{1}{2}$ h**

1. Express
   (a) 37 850 correct to 2 significant figures,
   (b) 47.56 cm correct to the nearest mm,
   (c) 75 489 cm^2 correct to the nearest 100 cm^2,
   (d) 1.3249 correct to 2 decimal places.   **[4]**

2. A group of pupils of a certain school named the subject they liked best. Their choices are represented on the given pie chart.
   (a) Show that the value of x is 32.
   (b) Calculate the percentage of the group who like Science.
   (c) Given that 48 pupils chose Mathematics, calculate the total number of pupils in the group.   **[4]**

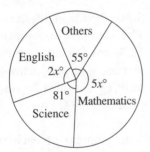

3. Simplify the following and give your answers as a fraction in its simplest form:

   (a) $3\frac{1}{4} + 1\frac{1}{4} \div \frac{3}{8}$

   (b) $5\frac{5}{8} - \left(\frac{2}{3}\right)^3 \div \sqrt{\frac{9}{16}}$ **[3]**

4. Find the H.C.F. and L.C.M. of 12, 28 and 64.   **[4]**

5. Evaluate the following:
   (a) $\{[(56 + 34) \div 5 - 7] \times 3 - 17\} \div 4$
   (b) $(-2)^2 - (7 - 8)^2 - (11 - 15)^3$ **[4]**

6. Add $4x^3 - 2x + 7$ to $x^3 + 5x^2 - x - 10$ and subtract the result from $x^2 + 7x^3 - 5x - 1$. **[3]**

7. Solve the equation

   $$\frac{3x - 2}{4} = \frac{x + 2}{5} - \frac{2x - 1}{10}.$$ **[3]**

8. Simplify the following expressions:
   (a) $2x - 2[3(1 - x) - 5(x - 2y)]$

   (b) $\frac{3}{4}x^2y \times \frac{5}{9}xz^3 \div \frac{20}{9}x^4y^2z$ **[4]**

9. (a) Find the radius of a circle if its area is 154 cm^2.   **[2]**
   (b) Find the volume of a solid cube whose total surface area is 150 cm^2.   **[2]**

10. All items in a shop were given a 20% discount during a sale. Find the original price of a calculator which was sold for $30.80.   **[3]**

11. (a) A driver travels the first 120 km of a 200-km journey at an average speed of 40 km/h. He travels the remaining journey at a speed of 60 km/h. Find the time taken for the whole journey.   **[3]**
    (b) A cyclist travels from A to B at a speed of 16 km/h and back from B at 24 km/h. If the total time taken is 5 hours, find the distance of AB.   **[3]**

12. Factorise each of the following
    (a) $3x + 12y + 24z$ **[1]**
    (b) $5h(3x + 2y) - 2k(2y + 3x)$ **[1]**
    (c) $3px + 2qh - 2qx - 3ph$ **[2]**

13. (a) The perimeter of a square is 24 cm. Find its area.   **[2]**
    (b) The length of a rectangle is twice its width and its perimeter is 24 cm. Find its area.   **[2]**

14. In the figure, $AB = BC$, $B\hat{A}C = 56°$ and CD is perpendicular to AB. Calculate the value of
(a) $A\hat{C}D$,　　　(b) $B\hat{C}D$.　　　**[4]**

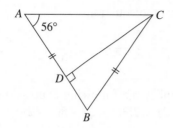

15. 40 students in a secondary one class were asked how many siblings they have. The table below illustrates the results of the survey.

Number of siblings	0	1	2	3	4	5
Number of students	8	9	x	7	3	1

(a) Find the value of x.　　　**[1]**
(b) Draw a histogram to show the data.　**[3]**
(c) If the above information is represented in a pie chart, find the angle representing students with 1 sibling.　　　**[1]**

16. Construct a trapezium $ABCD$ such that $A\hat{B}C = 85°$, $B\hat{C}D = 75°$, $AB = 6.5$ cm and $BC = 9.4$ cm. Measure and write down the length of AD and of CD.　　　**[5]**

17. (a) Given that $a = 2$, $b = 3$ and $c = -1$, evaluate each of the following:
(i) $2a^2 - 3b - 5c^2$
(ii) $\dfrac{5a - c}{b - c^2} + \dfrac{b + c^3}{a^3 - 2b}$　　　**[4]**

(b) Estimate the value of $\dfrac{8.03}{1.98}$, giving your answer correct to 1 significant figure. Use the result to estimate the value of $\dfrac{80.3}{0.0198}$.　　　**[2]**

18. (a) In the figure, AB is parallel to PQ. Find the value of x.　　　**[3]**

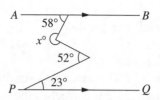

(b) Three interior angles of an n-gon are 153°, 144° and 100°. If the other $(n - 3)$ interior angles are each equal to 149°, find the value of n.　　　**[2]**

19. A racing driver completed a race of 351 km in 3 hours.
(a) Calculate his average speed in km/h.
(b) The car travelled $6\dfrac{1}{2}$ km on one litre of petrol on the average. Calculate the number of litres of petrol used.　　**[3]**

20. (a) Solve the inequality $3x - 5 > 2x + 4$. **[1]**
(b) The petrol consumption of a car is 12.4 km per litre. Find the minimum number of litres of petrol (in whole number of litre) that must be filled to complete a journey of 300 km.　　　**[2]**

21. Find the gradient of each of the following lines
(a) $y = 5 + 4x$
(b) $2x + 5y = 17$　　　**[2]**

22. (a) A piece of copper wire 200 m long has a diameter of 1.2 mm. Calculate its volume. If the density of copper is 8.9 g/cm³, calculate the mass of the wire.　**[4]**
(b) A trapezium has parallel sides $(2x - 3)$ cm and $(3x + 4)$ cm. If the height between the parallel sides is 12 cm and the area of the trapezium is 216 cm², calculate the value of x.　　　**[3]**

23. (a) A driver travels the first 240 km of a 600-km journey at an average speed of 60 km/h. If the time taken for the whole journey is 8 hours 48 minutes, find the average speed at which he travels the latter part of the journey.　　　**[3]**

(b) Given that
$$\frac{1}{2} - \frac{1}{3} = \frac{1}{6}$$
$$\frac{1}{3} - \frac{1}{4} = \frac{1}{12}$$
$$\frac{1}{4} - \frac{1}{5} = \frac{1}{20}$$
$$\vdots$$
$$\frac{1}{x} - \frac{1}{x+1} = \frac{1}{110},$$

write down
(i) the fourth line of the sequence, [1]
(ii) the value of x. [2]

24. Two cylindrical jars, A and B, have diameters $5x$ cm and $3x$ cm respectively. They are as shown in the diagram and not drawn to scale. Initially, cylinder A is empty and cylinder B contains water to a height of 20 cm. If all this water is poured into cylinder A, calculate the height of the water in it.

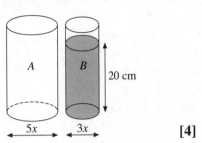

[4]

Answers
(Practice Questions, Tests and Specimen Papers)

Chapter 1

1. 129
2. 269
3. 107
4. 6
5. $3^2 \times 5 \times 7$
6. $2 \times 3 \times 7^2 \times 11$
7. $2^3 \times 7 \times 11 \times 13$
8. $2^4 \times 3^2 \times 5^2 \times 17$
9. $2^7 \times 3^3 \times 17$
10. $2^3 \times 5^2 \times 19 \times 31$
11. 8
12. 9
13. 14
14. 18
15. 8
16. 72
17. 6
18. 14
19. 12
20. 15
21. 21
22. 45
23. 120
24. 144
25. 525
26. 1215
27. 2448
28. 5544
29. 5880
30. 1305
31. 6552
33. 6804
34. 20 994
35. 1260
36. 21, 756
37. 45, 5040
38. 56, 4312
39. 252, 7056
40. 28, 1120
41. 63, 22 681
42. 66, 11 880
43. 35, 12 600
44. (i) 40 (ii) 212
    (iii) 16 and 36
    (iv) 1331 (v) 100
45. 169, 196, 225, 256, 289, 324, 343, 361, 400, 441, 484, 512, 529, 576
46. 48
47. 84
48. 45
49. 63
50. 96
51. 56
52. 91
53. 18
54. 21
55. 26
56. 34
57. 39
58. 400
59. 400
60. 642
61. 33 750
62. 3586
63. 2500
64. 4900
65. 90 000
66. 8000
67. 216 000
68. 64 000 000
69. 7
70. 4
71. 10
72. 25
73. 1020
74. 40 000
75. 7
76. 318 486
77. 74 279
78. 101 306
79. 69
80. 92
81. 120
82. (a) 21 (b) 5
    (c) 6
83. (a) 24 (b) 4
84. (a) 9 (b) 6

Chapter 2

1. +10
2. −91
3. −60
4. +14
5. (i) −1 (ii) 6
   (iii) 3 (iv) 0
   (v) 1
6. (i) −30 (ii) $-\frac{12}{2}$
   (iii) $-\frac{4}{5}$ (iv) −1
   (v) −13
7. −4
8. −14
9. −23
10. 0
11. 120
12. −720
13. −630
14. −1280
15. 360
16. 120
17. −8
18. −125
19. 3
20. 25
21. −5
22. −3
23. −6
24. −1
25. 8
26. −3
27. 1
28. 0
29. 1330 m
30. 20°C
31. 972, 987, 1010, 981, 1005, 991
32. (a) 4, −1, −2, 1
    (b) A (c) C
33. (a) −6, −52, 58, 98, 85
    (b) Bob (c) Den

Chapter 3

1. $-\frac{5}{6}$
2. $\frac{17}{30}$
3. $\frac{13}{15}$
4. $\frac{25}{36}$
5. $\frac{13}{20}$
6. $-\frac{7}{8}$
7. $1\frac{13}{20}$
8. $-3\frac{1}{18}$
9. $-2\frac{7}{12}$
10. $-13\frac{3}{4}$
11. $5\frac{2}{5}$
12. $3\frac{5}{12}$
13. $-2\frac{7}{20}$
14. $-\frac{3}{10}$
15. −12
16. 20
17. $-81\frac{1}{2}$
18. $\frac{1}{4}$
19. $-\frac{2}{21}$
20. $-3\frac{1}{30}$
21. $1\frac{1}{9}$
22. −4
23. $-1\frac{1}{44}$
24. −64
25. $\frac{2}{13}$
26. $-\frac{3}{11}$
27. $2\frac{5}{7}$
28. $4\frac{1}{4}$
29. −1
30. $-1\frac{1}{12}$
31. 2
32. $-\frac{3}{5}$
33. −3
34. $1\frac{3}{16}$
35. $-10\frac{11}{12}$
36. 4.925
37. 7.026
38. 0.515
39. −44.030
40. 32.165
41. 12.605
42. −7.651
43. 0.313
44. (a) $\frac{4}{5}$ (b) $\frac{1}{2}$
45. (a) $\frac{3}{5}$ (b) $\frac{11}{20}$
46. (a) $\frac{13}{15}$ (b) $\frac{23}{50}$

47. (a) $\frac{11}{25}$ (b) $\frac{7}{20}$

48. (a) $\frac{43}{48}$ (b) 0.815

49. $\frac{13}{20}, \frac{2}{3}, \frac{7}{10}$

50. $\frac{13}{20}, \frac{11}{15}, \frac{3}{4}$

51. $\frac{37}{45}, \frac{5}{6}, \frac{13}{15}$

52. $\frac{7}{18}, \frac{11}{27}, \frac{5}{12}$

53. $0.7, \frac{2}{3}, \frac{3}{5}$

54. $\frac{14}{25}, \frac{11}{20}, \frac{53}{100}, \frac{26}{50}$

55. $\frac{7}{9}, \frac{13}{18}, \frac{19}{27}, \frac{2}{3}$

56. $\frac{17}{24}, \frac{11}{16}, \frac{2}{3}, \frac{5}{8}$

57. $12   58. $\frac{1}{4}$, $28 000

59. $\frac{1}{6}$ 60. $1800

61. $0.\dot{5}$ 62. $0.7\dot{2}$

63. $0.25\dot{7}$ 64. $0.91\dot{6}$

65. $0.5\dot{1}$ 66. $1.6\dot{1}$

67. $0.84\dot{0}\dot{9}$ 68. $0.395\,8\dot{3}$

69. $0.763\dot{8}$ 70. $1.0\dot{4}$

71. $1.\dot{0}\dot{1}$ 72. $0.\dot{1}0\dot{0}$

73. 4.37   74. 16.1

75. 26.28   76. 51.95

77. 83.64   78. 5

79. 0.01   80. 7.12

81. 200   82. 34

83. 16   84. 8.1

85. 6.4   86. 579

Chapter 4
1. C   2. A
3. D   4. C
5. D   6. D
7. E   8. B
9. C   10. B
11. C   12. D
13. B   14. D
15. C   16. C

17. (i) 5.620 km
   (ii) 900 cm
   (iii) 32 000 g
   (iv) 50 kg
18. (i) 4 cm   (ii) 24 cm
   (iii) 107 cm   (iv) 655 cm
19. (i) 14.0 kg   (ii) 57.5 kg
   (iii) 108.4 kg   (iv) 763.2 kg
20. (i) 7.0 cm^2 (ii) 40.1 cm^2
   (iii) 148.3 cm^2
   (iv) 168.4 cm^2
21. 4.1   22. 0.0770
23. 5004   24. 20
25. 18.1   26. 3.91
27. 38   28. 18.14
29. 0.008 17   30. 240.0
31. 0.054   32. 0.0326
33. (i) 500 000   (ii) 0.2
   (iii) 3   (iv) 2000
   (v) 10 000
34. 80   35. 200
36. 6   37. 0.002
38. 7   39. 550 km
40. 12   41. $75
42. $100   43. 15 km/litre
44. 12 m^2
45. (a) $4000   (b) $47 900
46. 1200   47. 9
48. 20 minutes
49. (a) 30 m   (b) 50 m^2
50. (a) (i) 3000 mm
     (ii) 30 m
   (b) (i) 300 m^2
     (ii) 30 000 mm^2
51. 34.3   52. 26.9
53. 138.1   54. 36.1
55. 2.5   56. 18.5
57. 4.70   58. 26.80
59. 0.05   60. 14.94
61. 10.10   62. 8.10
63. 0.038   64. 8.445
65. 7.450   66. 11.639
67. 6.828   68. 32.929
69. 13.451   70. 4.826
71. 5.7555   72. 0.09
73. 9.226   74. 0.04

75. 37.129   76. 0.9
77. (i) 32.9688   (ii) 32.97
78. 0.007
79. (i) 0.056 088   (ii) 0.0561
80. (i) 9.625   (ii) 9.6
81. 57.425   82. 24.187
83. 0.051   84. 45.991
85. 42.641   86. 4.877
87. 36.303   88. 13
89. $51.52   90. $17.44
91. 23
92. (a) $4\frac{7}{10}$ (b) 4.7000
93. (a) $5\frac{41}{110}$ (b) 5.3727
94. (a) $3\frac{1}{828}$ (b) 3.0012
95. (a) $40\frac{5}{6}$ (b) 40.8333
103. (a) $81\frac{6}{7}$ (b) 81.8571

Chapter 5
1. $7x + 3y$ 2. $3x^3 + 2y^2$
3. $2x^2 - 4\sqrt[3]{y}$ 4. $\frac{1}{3}y$ or $\frac{y}{3}$
5. $27xh - \frac{k}{2y}$
6. $(x + y)^3 - \sqrt{15xy}$
7. 46   8. 99
9. -8 10. $\frac{5}{12}$
11. 18   12. 12
13. $-8\frac{1}{2}$ 14. 9
15. 11   16. 2
17. -105 18. $2a$
19. $2a$ 20. $2a + 3b$
21. $-4a - 9b$ 22. $3x + 3y + 4z$
23. $-2p - 3q + 4r$
24. $12xy - 17xz + 5yz$
25. $8abc$
26. $8a^2 - 11a + 4$
27. $9x^3 - 9x^2 + 5x$
28. $3\frac{1}{2}ab + bc$
29. $3x - 10y$
30. $31x + 27y$
31. $-100x + 18y$

32. $8p - 3q - 5r$

33. $6\frac{1}{2}a + 8b - 8c$

34. $-a^3 - 3a^2 - 2a$

35. $\dfrac{6b}{a}$ **36.** $\dfrac{10x}{9}$

37. $7x^3$ **38.** $\dfrac{9z^5}{16x^3y}$

39. $\dfrac{4z}{9}$ **40.** $\dfrac{9x^3}{4y^3}$

41. $\dfrac{8x}{5yz}$ **42.** $\dfrac{7x}{12}$

43. $\dfrac{7x - 10y}{8}$ **44.** $\dfrac{19x + 12y}{30}$

45. $\dfrac{25x - 66y}{42}$

46. $2a + 3b + 3c$

47. $7a^2 + 8c^2$

48. $2ab + 5bc + 5ac$

49. $9abc - 11bc + 7ac$

50. $\dfrac{1}{2}xy^2 + 1\dfrac{1}{4}xy$

51. $3x^3 + 2x^2 - 8$

52. $6x^4 - 13x^3 - 4x^2 + 26x$

53. $-6x^3 - 15x + 9$

54. $24a^3 - 12a^2 + 12a - 25$

55. $-6x^3 - 2x^2 - 3x + 16$

56. $x^3 + x^2 - 10x + 13$

57. $(x + 3)(y + 2)$

58. $(y - 2)(3x - 4)$

59. $(2y - 3)(3k - 2)$

60. $(2x - 5)(3x - y)$

61. $(p + 5q)(3x - 5)$

62. $4(h - 2)(3p + 2q)$

63. $2(3x + 2)(h - 3k)$

64. $2x(p - 2q)$

65. $2x(3h + 4k)$

66. $5(x - 2y)(3p + 2q - r)$

67. $(x + 2)(y + 5)$

68. $(a + 2b)(3x - y)$

69. $(5x - y)(3p - 2q)$

70. $(h - 2k)(3x + 7y)$

71. $(2x - 3y)(p - q)$

72. $(3u + 4v)(2h - 3k)$

Term I Revision Test

1. **(a)** 276 **(b)** 966

2. **(a)** **(i)** 0.325
  (ii) 1.5625
(b) **(i)** $\dfrac{49}{500}$ **(ii)** $1\dfrac{1}{16}$

3. **(a)** 8.45 **(b)** 0.070
(c) 26 000 **(d)** 16 000

4. **(a)** **(i)** $2^6 \times 3^2$
  (ii) $2^3 \times 3^6$; 24, 18
(b) **(i)** 28
  (ii) 9
(c) **(i)** 240 **(ii)** 1260

5. **(a)** 9 **(b)** -109
(c) $-5\dfrac{1}{7}$ **(d)** -134

6. **(a)** 1667.45 **(b)** 0.76
(c) 0.03 **(d)** 29.78

7. **(a)** $5(x + 3y)$
(b) $(x + 2y)(c - 3d)$

8. **(a)** $8a - 9$ **(b)** $5x + 3y$
(c) -14

9. **(a)** $2y - z$ **(b)** $5t - u + 3v$
(c) px **(d)** $2bm$
(e) $4pqy$

10. **(a)** 25 **(b)** 50 l
(c) 50

11. **(a)** 6 **(b)** -30
(c) $1\dfrac{1}{30}$

12. **(a)** 6.45×10^5
(b) 9.5×10^{-4}
(c) 3.44×10^8
(d) 7.3×10^{-4}

13. **(a)** 165° **(b)** 142°
(c) 72°

Chapter 6

1. 10 000, 100 000, 1 000 000
2. 120, 720, 5040
3. 26, 31, 36
4. 250, 1250, 6250
5. 125, 216, 343
6. 32, 27, 22 **7.** 17, 23, 30
8. 35, 41, 48 **9.** 59, 95, 144
10. 32, 16, 8 **11.** 38, 70, 134
12. 60, 40, 50 **13.** 24, 30
14. 25, 31 **15.** 250, 50

16. 23, 17 **17.** 24
18. 3
19. **(i)** $1 + 3 + 5 + 7 + 9 + 11 + 13 + 15 = 8^2$
  (ii) 12
20. **(a)** 21, 28, 36, 45;
  56, 84, 120, 165
(b) **(i)** $9^3 - 9 = 720 = 6 \times 120$;
    $10^3 - 10 = 990$
    $= 6 \times 165$
  (ii) $m = 8$, $n = 504$, $k = 6$
21. **(a)** 21, 34, 55, 89, 144
(b) **(ii)** $1^2 + 1^2 + 2^2 + 3^2 + 5^2$
    $+ 8^2 + 13^2 = 13 \times 21$
    $1^2 + 1^2 + 2^2 + 3^2 + 5^2$
    $+ 8^2 + 13^2 + 21^2$
    $= 21 \times 34$
    $1^2 + 1^1 + 2^2 + 3^2 + 5^2$
    $+ 8^2 + 13^2 + 21^2 + 34^2$
    $= 34 \times 55$
    $1^2 + 1^2 + 2^2 + 3^2 + 5^2$
    $+ 8^2 + 13^2 + 21^2 + 34^2$
    $+ 55^2 = 55 \times 89$
22. **(c)** 550, 803
23. **(b)** **(i)** 10, 22, 31
    (ii) 105, 212, 316
  (c) 14, 43
24. **(b)** **(i)** 120 **(ii)** 276
  (c) 20
25. 37, 42; $7 + 5n$
26. 53, 47; $89 - 6n$
27. 37, 44; $7n - 5$
28. 32, 64; 2^{n-1}
29. 486, 1458; $2 \times 3^{n-1}$
30. 2916, 8748; 4×3^n
31. 37, 43; $1 + 6n$
32. 19, 15; $43 - 4n$
33. $62\dfrac{1}{2}$, $31\dfrac{1}{4}$; $\dfrac{4000}{2^n}$
34. $9n - 3$; $k = 18$
35. $7n - 3$; $k = 24$
36. $3 \times 2^{n-1}$ or $\dfrac{3}{2} \times 2^n$; $r = 10$
37. $768 - 21n$; $k = 18$
38. $\dfrac{2048}{2^n}$; $h = 13$

Chapter 7

1. 5   **2.** 1

3. 3   **4.** $-6\frac{2}{3}$

5. $2\frac{10}{11}$ **6.** $-2\frac{1}{6}$

7. 20   **8.** 12.5

9. 30   **10.** 1.05

11. 13   **12.** 0.8

13. $6\frac{1}{3}$ **14.** 2

15. $-7\frac{1}{5}$ **16.** $-\frac{1}{4}$

17. $-2\frac{2}{7}$ **18.** 4

19. $1\frac{10}{11}$ **20.** $\frac{8}{17}$

21. 8   **22.** -2

23. -3 **24.** $4\frac{1}{2}$

25. $-1\frac{1}{11}$ **26.** $\frac{7}{12}$

27. 2.4   **28.** 12

29. -1.26 **30.** 27

31. $1\frac{2}{5}$ **32.** $-\frac{1}{2}$

33. $-1\frac{1}{8}$ **34.** $-1\frac{1}{2}$

35. $13\frac{1}{2}$ **36.** $-6\frac{2}{13}$

37. 4   **38.** $\frac{2}{3}$

39. $-17\frac{1}{3}$ **40.** $\frac{-8}{9}$

41. (i) 5750   (ii) 6000

42. $\frac{-8}{9}$ **43.** $-\frac{23}{30}$

44. 14, 18   **45.** 21

46. 24, 96   **47.** 72

48. 79, 81, 83   **49.** 40

50. 25, 27   **51.** 144

52. Ahmad — 18, Bobby — 9, John — 11

53. 13 yr   **54.** 2 yr

55. 11 yr   **56.** 20 yr, 4 yr

57. $420   **58.** 28

59. $48   **60.** 21

61. 330 cm^2

62. (a) $2\frac{2}{3}$ (b) $-7\frac{1}{2}$

(c) 30   (d) $\frac{3}{5}$

(e) $2\frac{1}{2}$ (f) $2\frac{1}{4}$

(g) 2

63. $x = 12$ **64.** $54

65. 5 hours

66. (a) $x > 11$ (b) $x > 5$

(c) $x < 8$ (d) $x < -1.6$

(e) $x < 2$ (f) $x < 0.5$

67. 8 teachers   **68.** 7 buses

69. $1.20   **70.** $135

Chapter 8

1. (a) 24 cm   (b) 1.6 cm
(c) 2.4 cm

2. (a) 21.6 cm   (b) 34.4 cm
(c) 312 mm

3. (a) 26 cm   (b) 4 m
(c) 14.2 cm

4. (a) 28.8 m   (b) 7.22 m
(c) 4.5 cm

5. 730   **6.** 46 500

7. 540   **8.** 260

9. 46.5   **10.** 20

11. 0.05   **12.** 0.065

13. 320 000

14. (a) 32 cm   (b) 2 cm
(c) 4.8 m

15. 28 cm   **16.** 3.9 m

17. 6 cm

18. (a) 441 cm^2 (b) 0.04 cm^2
(c) 0.0961 m^2

19. 168 cm^2 **20.** 0.9 m^2

21. 25.2 cm^2 **22.** 11.5 m^2

23. 2.4 cm^2 **24.** 140 cm^2

25. 0.72 m^2

26. (a) 62.8 cm
(b) 188.4 cm
(c) 3.768 m
(d) 25.12 cm
(e) 75.36 cm
(f) 188 cm

27. (a) 616 cm^2 (b) 55.44 cm^2

(c) 2464 cm^2
(d) 5544 mm^2
(e) 1386 cm^2

28. (a) 25 cm   (b) 40 m
(c) 78 mm   (d) 0.15 m
(e) 10 cm

29. 10 cm, 4 cm^2

30. 30 cm, 36 cm^2

31. 60 cm 144 cm^2

32. 70 cm, 196 cm^2

33. 108 cm^2 **34.** 72 cm^2

35. 53.5 cm^2 **36.** 645 cm^2

37. 144 cm^2 **38.** 60 cm^2

39. 144 cm^2 **40.** 288 cm^2

41. 251 cm^2 **42.** 93.5 cm^2

43. 126 cm, $943\frac{1}{4}$ cm^2

44. 94 cm, 593.25 cm^2

45. 90 cm, $544\frac{1}{4}$ cm^2

46. 120 cm, 448 cm^2

47. 201 cm^2; 100 cm

48. 114 cm^2, 119 cm

49. 490 cm^2, 163 cm

50. 456 cm^2, 119 cm

51. 55.0 cm^2, 82.2 cm

52. 124 cm^2, 75.4 cm

53. 15.3 cm^2, 29.7 cm

54. 226 cm^2, 75.4 cm

55. 31.5   **56.** 393.75 cm^2

57. (a) 24 cm   (b) 226.08 cm^2

58. 314 cm^2 **59.** 584 cm^2

60. 972 cm^2 **61.** 0.72 ha

62. (a) $11 200   (b) $9600

63. 11 litres, $71.50

64. (a) $x = 6.3$ (b) $k = 9\frac{5}{8}$
(c) $h = 13$ (d) $y = 44$

65. $x = 2.5$, 56 cm^2, 30 cm^2, No

66. 153.36 cm^2

67. 84 cm^2

68. 282 cm^2, 73.7 cm

Chapter 9

1. 125 cm^3, 150 cm^2

2. 13.824 cm^3, 34.56 cm^2

3. 9000 cm³, 2820 cm²

4. 0.432 m³, 3.72 m²

5. 216 cm² 6. 1.5 m²

7. 73.5 cm² 8. 3375 m³

9. 2.197 cm³ 10. $15\frac{5}{8}$ mm³

11. 3000 12. 15 400

13. 5100

14. $1350, $675, $6930, $1404, $2295

15. 40 16. 960

17. 7560 18. 5.63 g/cm³

19. 5.40 g/cm³ 20. 5.90 g/cm³

21. 3.82 g/cm³

22. 972 cm³, 684 cm²

23. 1344 cm³, 864 cm²

24. 288 cm³, 360 cm²

25. 336 cm³, 384 cm²

26. 2520 cm³, 1364 cm²

27. 880 cm³, 728 cm²

28. (a) 6.72 litres
    (b) 892.5 cm²
    (c) 1116 g

29. (a) 158.4 litres
    (b) 28 270 cm³
    (c) 25.44 kg

30. 38 020 cm³, 6790 cm²

31. 9.251 cm³, 25.98 cm²

32. 110 900 cm³, 12 850 cm²

33. 1952 cm³, 949.5 cm²

34. 5 cm 35. 1.118 cm

36. 20 cm 37. 5.40 cm

38. 0.940 cm 39. 7.64 cm

40. $6\frac{2}{3}$ cm 41. 2.29 g/cm³

42. 63.04 kg 43. 2.4 m

44. 10 cm 45. 27

46. 18 47. 50 cm

48. 48 cm 49. 50

50. 15 51. 45.47 cm

52. 250 m³ 53. 52 278 m³

54. 12.1 cm

55. 336 900 cm³; 91 875 cm³

56. 450 m³, 450 tonnes

57. 3.072 m³

58. 5340 cm³, 4.005 kg

59. 10.7 cm, 2575 cm²

60. 92 687.5 cm³, 88.05 kg, 1566.45 kg

Term II Revision Test

1. (a) (i) 32, 64
       (ii) 2208, 4416;
            $32 \times 69 = 2208$,
            $64 \times 69 = 4416$
   (b) (i) $13 \times 69 = 69 + 276 + 552$
            $= 897$
            $(13 = 1 + 4 + 8)$
       (ii) 29×69
            $= 69 + 276 + 552 + 1104$
            $= 2001$
            $(29 = 1 + 4 + 8 + 16)$
       (iii) 76×69
            $= 276 + 552 + 4416$
            $= 5244 \ (76 = 4 + 8 + 64)$

2. (a) $\frac{2}{3}$ (b) 6
   (c) $2\frac{1}{2}$

3. (a) 31 (b) 30 yr, 8 yr

4. (a) 40, 20 (b) 45 m

5. (a) $2\frac{1}{7}$ (b) $\frac{3}{4}$

6. $1\frac{7}{25}$

7. 10 min 41 s

8. 169 cm²

9. 924 l; 96.25 cm

10. 258.72 cm²

11. 7.7 cm²

12. (a) $x < 7$ (b) $x > 9$

13. 48 200 cm², 480 000 cm³

Mid-Year Specimen Paper

1. (a) $2\frac{4}{9}$ (b) $6\frac{17}{18}$

2. $36y - 151x$

3. (a) 47, 50 (b) 96, 145

4. (a) 0 (b) −3

5. 2

6. (a) (i) 27 (ii) 27.0
   (b) 200 (c) 0.769

7. (a) 41 (b) $4n + 1$
   (c) 101

9. (a) $\frac{5}{6}, \frac{11}{13}, \frac{8}{9}$
   (b) 111, 119

10. (a) 336 (b) 6

11. 12 yr, 18 yr

12. $\frac{5}{8}$

13. (a) $3(x + 6y + 9z)$
    (b) $(a + 3b)(2x - y)$

14. $\frac{4}{15}x + 1\frac{7}{15}$

15. $340, $1870

16. 25 m

17. 42 cm²

18. (a) 5 (b) $\frac{7}{30}$

19. (a) T (b) F
    (c) F (d) T
    (e) T

20. (a) (i) 62.4 (ii) −2710
    (b) $16a$

21. (a) 0.42, $0.4\dot{2}$, $0.42\dot{8}$, $0.4\dot{2}\dot{8}$, $\frac{3}{7}$
    (b) 33

22. (a) 7 yr, 17 yr (b) $s(q - p)$

23. (a) 23, 24 (b) 27, 36

24. (a) (i) 32, 41 (ii) 25, −36
        (iii) $\frac{9}{11}, \frac{5}{6}$ (iv) 27, 40
    (b) (i) 40.26 (ii) 0.01 342

25. (a) $x \geq 11$ (b) $x \geq -13$

Chapter 10

1. 2 : 5 2. 4 : 7

3. 9 : 8 4. 3 : 11

5. 9 : 16 6. 19 : 11

7. 64 : 25 8. 27 : 64

9. 1 : 6 10. 3 : 7

11. 3 : 4 12. 3 : 1

13. 3 : 1 14. 9 : 2

15. 1 : 15 16. 4 : 1

17. 3 : 4 18. 3 : 10

19. 5 : 24 20. 3 : 8

21. 27 : 16 22. 14 : 5

23. 2 : 3 24. 2 : 1

25. $9 : 3 : 5$ **26.** $3 : 1 : 7$
27. $2 : 3 : 7$ **28.** $29 : 10 : 13$
29. $23 : 17 : 5$ **30.** $1 : 3 : 2$
31. $9 : 20$ **32.** $1 : 5$
33. $10 : 3$ **34.** $5 : 1$
35. $7 : 12$ **36.** $3 : 4$
37. $8 : 3$ **38.** $1 : 3$
39. \$56 : \$280   **40.** \$210 : \$126
41. \$140, \$196   **42.** \$72, \$264
43. \$120, \$216   **44.** \$63, \$273
45. \$128, \$208   **46.** \$160, \$176
47. \$154, \$182   **48.** \$98, \$238
49. (a) (i) \$20 (ii) \$36
    (iii) \$15 (iv) \$12
    (v) \$30 (vi) \$18
   (b) (i) \$120
    (ii) \$90
    (iii) \$105
    (iv) \$132
    (v) \$110
    (vi) \$117
50. (i) 36 (ii) 72
   (iii) 90 (iv) 63
51. (i) \$18 (ii) \$36
   (iii) \$123 (iv) \$186
52. (a) (i) $173°$ (ii) $118°$
    (iii) $85°$
   (b) (i) $119°$
    (ii) $154°$
    (iii) $175°$
53. (a) (i) \$480
    (ii) \$760
    (iii) \$1720 (iv) \$22 800
   (b) (i) \$216 (ii) \$342
    (iii) \$774 (iv) \$10 260
54. (ii) \$80 (iii) \$88
   (iv) \$68
55. (i) \$156 (ii) \$252
   (iii) \$720 (iv) \$1080
56. (i) $5 : 6$ (ii) $13 : 14$
   (iii) $11 : 9$ (iv) $7 : 20$
57. $4 : 9$ **58.** $8 : 5$
59. (i) $4 : 3$ (ii) $4 : 1;\ 1 : 3$
60. 24 m, $7 : 8$
61. $40 : 15 : 26$
62. $2 : 3$

63. (i) $4 : 5$ (ii) $16 : 25$
64. 18 35   **65.** 9 h
66. (i) $10\frac{1}{2}$ h (ii) 62 km/h
67. Paul, 1 h 55 min
68. (i) $8\frac{3}{4}$ h (ii) \$15.30
69. (a) (i) 3 h
     (ii) 2 h 24 min
     (iii) 1 h 20 min
   (b) 15 km/h
70. 45 km/h, 40 min
71. 18 20   **72.** 12
73. 8   **74.** 22
75. $3\frac{4}{5}$ **76.** $4\frac{1}{2}$
77. $2\frac{2}{5}$
78. (a) (i) \$45 (ii) \$99
   (b) (i) 35 m^2 (ii) 42 m^2
79. (a) (i) \$40.50 (ii) \$216
   (b) (i) 32 (ii) 18
    (iii) 60 (iv) 44
80. \$1.25   **81.** 320 km
82. \$79.06   **83.** \$22.36, 378
84. (i) \$4050 (ii) 5
85. (i) 6 h 25 min
   (ii) 693 km
86. 02 52 the next day
87. $77\frac{1}{2}$ **88.** 28
89. 15 28, 5 h 40 min, 48 km/h
90. 2 m^2
91. (i) 1 h 24 min
   (ii) 12 53
92. 9 h
93. (i) 7 days (ii) \$1680
   (iii) 24 h (iv) \$2040
94. 22   **95.** 70

Chapter 11

1. $2\frac{1}{10}$ **2.** $\frac{6}{125}$
3. $\frac{9}{50}$ **4.** $\frac{1}{400}$
5. $\frac{1}{75}$ **6.** 0.99
7. 3   **8.** 0.028

9. 0.0068   **10.** 0.010 02
11. 75%   **12.** 40%
13. 24%   **14.** 95%
15. 80%   **16.** 7%
17. 5.8%   **18.** 14%
19. 2.7%   **20.** 52.18%
21. 243%   **22.** $33\frac{1}{3}$ %
23. $8\frac{1}{3}$ %   **24.** $444\frac{4}{9}$ %
25. 125%   **26.** 25%
27. $33\frac{1}{3}$ %   **28.** $17\frac{1}{2}$ %
29. $33\frac{1}{3}$ %   **30.** $133\frac{1}{3}$ %
31. 48 litres   **32.** 1.8 kg
33. \$187.50   **34.** 21 cm
35. 16 m   **36.** 1030 people
37. \$66   **38.** 36 g
39. 18.9 m^2 **40.** 112.5 m
41. \$83.60   **42.** 56 g
43. 93 litres   **44.** 189 m
45. 400   **46.** 1000
47. 648   **48.** 280
49. 112   **50.** 125
51. 153   **52.** 45
53. 25%
54. 840, 4680, 5040
55. 1360, 1576, 1440, 1520, 1488
56. 70%, 30%
57. 51 kg   **58.** $93\frac{1}{3}$ %
59. 26%, 42%, 8%, 10%, 14%
60. \$1800   **61.** \$400
62. \$524.25
63. \$3.60, 45 cents
64. \$248.40   **65.** \$1836
66. (i) \$1080 (ii) \$3000
   (iii) \$480, $13\frac{1}{3}$ %
67. (i) \$76.50 (ii) \$2286
68. \$26 640   **69.** \$240 000
70 \$37.95   **71.** 38
72. 175   **73.** \$33
74. 50%   **75.** 25%
76. \$800, $31\frac{1}{4}$ %
77. gained \$8100

78. $425, gain 20%

79. 15%

80. 792 francs

Chapter 12

1. $A(1, 2)$, $B(7, 1)$, $C(-2, -3)$
$D(-4, 5)$, $E(6, 6)$, $F(3, -2)$
$G(-6, -2)$, $H(5, 0)$, $I(0, -5)$
$J(-7, 4)$, $L(-3, 0)$, $M(0, 3)$
$N(-5, 2)$, $O(0, 0)$, $P(6, -4)$
$Q(-3, -6)$, $R(4, -6)$

3. (a) isosceles $\triangle$
 (b) right-angled $\triangle$
 (c) rectangle
 (d) trapezium
 (e) kite
 (f) square
 (g) parallelogram
 (h) rhombus

4. 16 units^2

5. $l_1 = 1$, $l_2 = 2$, $l_3 = -1$

6. $AB = 1$, $BC = -2$, $AC = 0$

7. $PQ = 0$, $PR = -1\frac{1}{2}$, $QR = 1\frac{1}{2}$

8. (a) $S(-2, 0)$
 (b) $PQ = \frac{1}{2}$, $QR = -2$, $SR = \frac{1}{2}$
 (c) they have the same gradient, PQ is parallel to SR

9. $1, 0, -1$; $gi = -1$

10. $-1, 2, 3$
 (b) $(3, 2.5)$ does,
 $\left(-1, -\frac{1}{2}\right)$ does not
 (c) $(-2, 0)$ (d) $\frac{1}{2}$

11. (b) $1\frac{1}{2}, \frac{1}{3}, -2, -\frac{1}{4}$
 (c) $(0, 2)$

12. (b) $\frac{1}{2}, -1$ (c) $(2, 4)$

13. $50, 65, 80, 95$
 (b) $72.50 (c) 3 h 40 min
 (d) $gi = 15$,
 the change for each hour of work done.

14. (a) $7, 13, 19, 25$
 (c) 10°C

(d) 3.5 hours later

(e) 6, the rate of increase in temperature per hour

(f) the initial temperature of the chicken when it was taken from the freezer.

Chapter 13

1. (a) (i) 60 cars (ii) 90 cars
 (b) (i) 8 cars (ii) $5\frac{1}{2}$ cars
 (c) (i) 130 cars (ii) 100 cars
 (d) Tuesday
 (e) Wednesday
 (f) 50 cars
 (g) These are rest days for the production workers.
 (h) 480 cars

2. (a) (i) 48 kg (ii) 49.5 kg
 (iii) 52 kg
 (b) (i) February
 (ii) June
 (iii) August
 (c) November
 (d) May, October and December
 (e) 7.5 kg
 (f) (i) May (ii) November
 (g) October
 (h) Line graph

3. (a) 4th week
 (b) 5th week and 6th week
 (c) 9th week
 (d) Many pupils stayed away to prepare for the coming exam.
 (e) $66\frac{2}{3}\%$
 (f) 2nd and 3rd weeks, 15 pupils

4. (a) (i) $700 000
 (ii) $1 100 000
 (iii) $1 400 000
 (b) 2003
 (c) 2004 and 2005, $500 000
 (d) $300 000, $23\frac{1}{13}\%$
 (e) $250 000, $17\frac{6}{7}\%$
 (f) $6 300 000

5. (a) Monday of the first week. 24°C
 (b) Friday of the first week, 31°C
 (c) 4 days (d) $\frac{3}{5}$
 (e) (i) 28.4°C
 (ii) 29°C (iii) 29°C

7. (b) Monday (c) $\frac{1}{20}$
 (d) No
 (e) (i) 2.2 (ii) 4
 (iii) 2

8. (b) between 5 months and 6 months
 (c) at 7 months (d) 6.7 kg

9. (a) 1999, 2003, 2004
 (b) 2004, 2003
 (c) 2000, 2001, 2004, 2005, 2006, 2007
 (d) 2006, 2002
 (e) 1998, 2000, 2001, 2002, 2007

10. Yes. A bigger teacup may lead the customer to think that coffee is being served in bigger volumes in 2006, rather than the sales have increased.

11. 81°, 54°, 723°, 108°, 45°

12. 153°, 96°, 36°, 15°, 60°

13. (a) $\frac{17}{23}$ (b) $\frac{30}{17}$
 (c) (i) 23 million dollars
 (ii) 30 million dollars

14. (a) 171° (b) 24
 (c) $\frac{24}{35}$ (d) $29\frac{1}{6}\%$

15. (a) $34\frac{13}{18}\%$ (b) $\frac{17}{30}$
 (c) (i) 0.625 kg
 (ii) 0.45 kg
 (iii) 0.3 kg

16. (a) (i) 50%
 (ii) 20%
 (b) 54

18. (a) 35 (b) 1
 (c) 21 (d) $\frac{24}{25}$

20. (a) 35 (b) $51\frac{3}{7}\%$